TOWARD MANHOOD

HERMAN N. BUNDESEN, M.D.

Toward Manhood

J. B. LIPPINCOTT COMPANY

Philadelphia and New York

Library of Congress catalog card number 51–11205

CONTENTS

PREFACE

A Word to Parents, Teachers and Counselors

Although boys and girls today have the benefit of better sex instruction than in former years, most young people still have far too little knowledge of its most important aspects. As a doctor to whom many people have brought their saddest and most intimate stories; as the Health Commissioner for many years of a great city, I have perhaps had an unusual opportunity to observe the many ways in which ignorance of the true implications of sex can bring promising young lives to grief.

There are two kinds of ignorance. One is lack of information about bodily processes, and the consequences that may ensue from the misuse of sex. The other is false information, or information colored by unwholesome and unsocial attitudes. Either can be disastrous to the young person who as yet does not have the experience to form his own scale of values. No high school chemistry teacher would take a beginning class into a laboratory filled with ingredients for making explosives, and leave them there with no more guidance than to say, "Don't blow yourselves up!" Yet that is precisely the situation in which many teenagers are left when it comes to sex.

Parents, of course, are traditionally responsible for this

7

phase of teaching, and most, I am sure, would sincerely like to discharge their duty. But many adults cannot even talk to each other about sex. Some can tell dirty stories and jokes, and make a display of being worldly and sophisticated in matters of love. But they find themselves blocked when it comes to talking sensibly and seriously to their own youngsters. Some parents lack the vocabulary they think they need, and prefer to wait for the day when their children will find out the facts for themselves. If adults cannot talk about sex among themselves, they can scarcely be expected to discuss it with their children, or to tell them what to do about their sex feelings.

Many adults suffer from a too severely repressed kind of training which makes them unable to hear sex discussed without an emotional upset, although they may realize that they should have an understanding of this subject that is realistic and in accordance with the facts. They may even be ashamed to seek enlightening books on the subject. Lacking adequate information, they resort to a standard folklore, and picture a simplified romantic version of love and mating, with no regard for the difficulties and responsibilities involved.

This same folklore—and here is a point where many of us are inclined to err—depicts a standard adolescent with standard sex drives and standard childhood backgrounds, when as a matter of fact there is no such standard. Each adolescent is different from all others, depending upon his physiology at the moment, his early childhood experiences, and whether he is bright or dull, aggressive or shy, sexually wise or uninformed, and many other factors.

Perhaps the most handicapped parents of all are the ones who believe they know all there is to know, and may be unable to recognize that there are viewpoints that are saner and wiser than theirs. When adults are overly self-assured and feel no need of further information, they reject and resent opportunities to learn and to improve their attitudes. There isn't much that their children can do about them.

And then, parents who have the best will in the world, often find themselves at a loss when adolescence arrives. Many a mother has told me of an incident when a fourteen-year-old or a fifteen-year-old son would ask her for the explanation of some filthy, obscene thing he had heard. How much should a boy be told of the seamy side of life? Where is the dividing line between giving information, and putting troubling ideas into the mind of a teen-ager?

Hence, in spite of avowals that they will give their children a good sex education, a great many parents find themselves unable to carry it out, and this is particularly true when it comes to the things that teen-agers most want, and need, to know. It falls upon other adults to fill the breach, if a boy is to get correct information and develop a wholesome attitude toward sex. How many times is the family doctor called upon by the parents themselves to explain a subject in which they feel their own ignorance, or are barred by false modesty from discussing with their offspring! Indeed, anyone who works with children or young people may find himself (or herself) placed in the role of a sex educator.

Nor is this always, by any means, because parents have been remiss. Sex questions may arise quite naturally and spontaneously out of activities or studies in which a group or class or an individual is engaged. These are opportunities that should not be missed, for the information gained in this way falls quite naturally into place with other types of information, and accomplishes more than a portentous "heart to heart" talk that has been arranged in advance.

Not only a doctor, therefore, or a Boy Scout leader or a Y.M.C.A. director, may be confronted with the necessity of giving sex facts frankly and honestly. A teacher, a librarian, a school nurse, may find herself in the same situation. Juvenile Court judges deal constantly with sex problems. Any leader of a youth group, whether in a church or a boys' organization, any school authority, should be prepared to handle wisely and understandingly questions and situations of this type.

This preface is addressed, therefore, not to parents alone, but to all adults who work with boys and who have their interests at heart. You should be complimented if your son, or someone else's son, does bring such a question or problem to you. Boys do this only with persons they respect and whose objectivity and wisdom they trust.

We must realize that sexual maturity is a process in general development, and that when the sexual attitudes have an element of fear or disgust or depravity, the individual will fail to become a well-integrated and effective personality. The purpose of sex education is not to make youngsters fear sex. It is to help turn them into competent adults, able to express sexuality freely and with satisfaction, but at the same time to manage and control it within the restrictions of society.

The boy who has reached the adolescent years is entitled to know all we can tell him. In the streets and alleys he will hear crude words, smutty stories and ugly innuendoes which, while they give him knowledge of a kind, also prevent the growth of an appreciation of the fundamental rightness of all the functions of the body, when they are rightly used.

The adolescent boy is looking forward to taking his place in the adult world. He is intensely curious as to the things that will be expected of him there, and he should be. When he matures physically, he is subject to strong impulses which he doesn't understand, and which he needs to understand. His mind is grappling with a host of phenomena, both physical and social.

Mentally, he is equipped to deal with the true and correct information that he receives. The boy of this age can understand physics, chemistry, nuclear science, and the intricacies of machinery. He can possibly drive a car more expertly than his father—this is often the case. He can understand human feelings and emotions in the same way if he is given the same kind of accurate information in these that our society takes such pains to give him in other things.

In talking to an adolescent boy about sex, or the relationship of men and women, we are no longer dealing with a child. We are dealing with an individual who is soon to be an adult and who is right now forming his impressions of the adult world. His reasoning faculties are developed—we should be able to explain and defend any viewpoint we wish him to accept. We should remember that his own viewpoints may be colored by inaccurate information, or by emotions arising out of personal experiences. Patience and understanding, interest in him as an individual, will alone be effective in helping him get misconceptions straightened out.

He must be able to have confidence in us. He must feel that we are square shooters, and that we do our best to practice what we preach. If we don't know the answers, then we should be willing to try to help him find them.

This book is an attempt to lay before boys the whole subject of sex and the part it plays in one's life as frankly, as truthfully, as completely, as it is in my power to do. All my years of experience as a father, a doctor, a health commissioner who has seen the worst side of one of the largest cities in the world, have gone into it. It is what I have said to many boys. It is what I would say to every boy if I could.

It cannot, of course, answer all individual problems—no book can do that. It is my hope that any boy who reads it may know some understanding, sympathetic, fair-minded adult with whom he can talk over whatever special situation is troubling him; someone who will realize that he doesn't want to do wrong, but wishes an adult viewpoint as to what is right or wrong in a given instance. Boys don't deliberately want to ruin their lives and those of other people, any more than they want to blow themselves up in a chemical laboratory.

Nearly all boys and girls are, by nature, wholesome and clean. They do not naturally seek the vulgar. The normal boy wants to be manly and fine. The normal girl desires to be sweet and womanly. If we deal with them honestly and thoughtfully; if we see to it that first impressions are wisely and truthfully made; if we tell them, simply and reverently, the wonder and beauty that lie in the right kind of sex life and the way to attain it, we need not fear.

HERMAN N. BUNDESEN, M.D.

1. How Human Beings Reproduce

Any boy or young man who reads this book knows something—perhaps a great deal—about the way human beings reproduce. Yet we doctors find that the average person in reality has a rather sketchy and superficial knowledge of the workings of his or her own body, and particularly of the parts having to do with creating life.

I have known women who have borne a number of children, and yet have only the vaguest idea about how their bodies have brought about this marvelous feat. There are many men who know vulgar terms for the sex organs and sex activities, but not the scientific ones. (I remember one adult patient who constantly referred to his genital organs as his "generals.") Many who are well informed in other respects have little or no understanding of the intricate internal mechanisms, the way the various glands and organs work together to bring about fertilization of an ovum and the development of an infant.

As a matter of fact, it was not until fairly recently that science itself has known much more than the obvious and superficial facts about human reproduction. It is the late researches into the hitherto little known working of glands, and of the hormones they secrete, that have given us our realization of what a marvelously intricate and delicate mechanism it is that is responsible for carrying on the race.

We still do not understand it all, and perhaps will not for many years. But the more we know of it, the more fascinating a study it becomes. Mankind has never invented a machine, and I daresay never will, that can compare with the one Nature has given us for the perpetuation of the species.

We have long been aware, of course, that every living thing is endowed with a strong urge to maintain and to reproduce life. Not only is this a strong urge but one which, when carried out in human mating, is meant to give pleasure. If this urge were not present, animals and men might not wish to mate, and life would not continue.

But for mankind, mating in the untrammeled way the animals practise would be disastrous to the kind of civilization our superior brains are capable of developing. Mankind must put restraints on the sexual urges. Each of us therefore needs to understand his bodily mechanism and that of the opposite sex so that he will not be swept by animal instincts into behavior of a kind that is harmful for human beings.

There are some people—many of them, I fear—who would disagree with me about this. They would try to inhibit sex activity by making it seem evil, wicked. As a doctor, however, I know that looking upon sex in this way develops guilt feelings and neuroses. For the sexual urge, like hunger, is one of the driving forces of life. It will not be denied. And when it is accompanied by real love and respect for the partner, it is a source of great happiness and fulfillment. Turning the sex urge into something hidden and shameful is to breed mental illness and unhappiness.

I believe that boys who have reached the stage of adolescence are entitled to know as much about the sex processes as it is in my power to tell. By the time you have matured sexually, your brains have also attained full growth. This does not mean that you may not alter many of your present opinions and attitudes, as you learn from experience and from study. But your thinking mechanism is all there. And my experience with young people has been that they can be depended upon to draw the right conclusions, if they are given full and accurate data on which to base them.

In these first chapters I may be presenting some material that is old stuff to you, but I ask your indulgence. When my sons were learning to drive a car, I noticed that they lifted up the hood and wanted to know the names of the engine parts and the function of each one. That is a trait of the young male, and a very fine one. I wasn't always able to tell my sons everything they wanted to know about a gasoline engine. But as a doctor who has dissected human beings and treated their ailments, I may know some things about the sexual processes that have not come your way before. While this book is really about the emotional and social aspects of sex, I hope you will bear with me if I use the physiological side as a basis for our later discussions.

Every intelligent man and every intelligent woman should know the correct, scientific names for the male and female organs and glands of reproduction. As you get older, it is quite likely that you will hear these referred to, and you will want to know what they mean. Therefore, at the end of the chapters on the female and male reproduction organs I am giving you a list of the scientific terms for the various body parts concerned with reproduction. If you will study the sketches too, I believe you will have a pretty good idea of these processes—which, I am sorry to say, is more than most people have!

Female Reproductive System

I shall start with the female, for the female of course, has the major function in the production of life. Her body contours and her whole anatomy are designed for this. As you probably know, most of the female reproductive apparatus is inside the pelvis. It is for this reason that the average woman has a broader pelvis than the average man —it holds the reproductive organs, it must house a baby until the infant is developed enough to live in the outside world, and the opening through the pelvic bones must be large enough for the baby to emerge.

The principal internal female reproductive organs are the uterus, or womb; the ovaries, from which come the ova, or eggs; and the vagina, which is the passageway to the uterus from the outside of the body. The vagina, also called the birth canal, is about four inches long, and is lined with mucous membrane similar to the lining of one's mouth. Its elastic walls, formed of a network of muscles which can contract and also expand, are about three-quarters of an inch thick.

The uterus, to which the vagina leads, is normally about the size and shape of a pear, and like the vagina is a muscular organ. An ovary lies on each side of the uterus, and is attached to it by a broad ligament. The ovaries are oval, or egg-shaped, somewhat smaller than a testicle. They have two kinds of tissue—one which has to do with the production of eggs, and one which manufactures a female hormone called estrogen. Estrogen plays a large part in a woman's feeling of well-being. Inside the ovary are the Graafian follicles. Each of these is a tiny sac, containing an infinitesimal egg.

Just above the ovaries, and extending out from either side of the uterus like arms which end in a number of fingers, are the Fallopian tubes, one for each ovary. These delicate filaments—they are only about four inches long and are very small in circumference—are muscular canals. The finger-like fringes on the ends of the tubes are open, and they are close to the ovary, their function being to carry the ripened egg to the uterus.

The external portion of the female reproductive organ is called the vulva. This too is a rather elaborate mechanism of a number of parts, which are called the labia majora, labia minora, mons Veneris, clitoris, perineum and vestibulum vaginae. If you know your Latin you will have no trouble in identifying the vestibulum vaginae as the outer opening of the vagina. In most girls a thin incomplete membrane called the hymen lies just a little way inside the entrance. Nature has arranged for fluids from the uterus to pass through the opening in this membrane, and for it to be ruptured easily, with just a little bleeding, by the first entrance of the male penis. (Though in a few women the hymen is so tough that it must be clipped by a surgeon before intercourse is possible.)

Various peoples have attached great store to an unruptured hymen as a proof of virginity. Today, physicians in examining and treating a virgin do not disturb the hymen unless it is absolutely necessary to do so. However, not all women are born with a hymen, and it can be ruptured in other ways than through intercourse—by exercise, for instance. So the fact that a girl does not have a hymen does not necessarily mean that she is not a virgin.

Just above the vaginal opening is a little protuberance called the clitoris, and it corresponds in some ways to the male penis. (In fact, in the embryo infant, the same materials are used to build a penis in a boy, and a clitoris in a girl, and the clitoris has some erectile power.) Ordinarily only the tip of the clitoris can be seen, the rest of the organ nestling in the vulvar tissues. It is provided with very sensitive nerve endings, and is an important source of erotic satisfaction for the female, though not necessarily the most important one. Just below the clitoris is the urethra, the opening from the bladder. The perineum is the tissue extending between the vagina and the anus.

Enclosing these organs are first the labia minora, or inner lips, which are thin tissues containing many blood vessels; and next the labia majora, or outer lips, which are two thick folds of skin, lined with a delicate pink membrane.

Just above the vulva, and covered with hair in the mature female, is the mons Veneris, a mound of fatty tissue. It is from the mons Veneris that the labia majora extend, down almost to the anus. This whole area is extremely sensitive, and provided profusely, as in the vagina, with the nerve endings which contribute the pleasurable sensations of the mating act. Numerous small glands secrete fluids which keep the vulva moist.

Completing the female reproductive organs are the breasts—rudimentary in the male, but fully developed in the mature woman. In the female, these are in reality mammary glands, whose function of course is to produce milk. They are tipped with nipples, which are capable of growing larger and erecting under stimulation. In addition to the function they serve in nourishing a baby, the breasts and nipples are a part of the apparatus for pleasurable sensations in the mature female, and have an erotic appeal for the male. (A feature which is much played upon commercially, at present, and is often emphasized in feminine fashions, I might add.)

This is the reproductive system with which a girl baby is born, and it is believed that in her ovaries are thousands of immature eggs, or a supply sufficient to last several lifetimes. For as you study natural history, you will be impressed with Nature's lavishness in supplying the materials for reproduction, making every possible allowance for waste. Most of the eggs degenerate, however, and all remain immature until a girl reaches the age of twelve or thirteen.

That is when the female reproductive cycle begins with most girls, though some start it earlier, and some considerably later than others. I think we ought to go into this monthly cycle at some length, for I find that it is something understood by few men, outside of the medical profession. Few women, in fact, know much about it except for the manifestation at the end of the cycle, which is menstruation, and they are inclined to keep menstruation a secret except from their husbands and doctors.

To begin with, we now know that this cycle is not a matter of the sex organs alone, and menstruation is by no means the most important part of it. The cycle is controlled from the anterior lobe of the pituitary gland, which is connected with the brain and secretes a number of important hormones. At the beginning of the cycle, one of these hormones stimulates the ovaries into action, in rather the same way that an electrical impulse starts a gasoline engine. The ovaries then begin to manufacture estrogen in large amounts. As we have seen, estrogen gives women a feeling of well-being. Therefore, while this is going on, a girl or woman usually feels her best self. Normally she is outgoing, cheerful, peppy, this happy feeling coming to a peak at the time of ovulation, which we will consider in a minute.

At the same time that the ovaries start their manufacture of estrogen, an ovum begins to ripen in its little sac. (With puberty, the sacs, or follicles, move up to the surface of the ovary.) When the egg is matured, it pushes through the surface of the ovary, the sac breaks, and the egg is released to enter the Fallopian tube. Slowly it makes its way toward the uterus. This is what is meant by ovulation—the freeing of the ripened egg from the ovary.

Meanwhile the estrogens the ovaries are turning out so prolifically are working on the uterus lining. At the start of the cycle, the lining of the uterus is a thin structure, almost devoid of glands. But by the time ovulation takes place, the estrogens have built the womb lining into a thicker tissue with greater blood supply.

There is still work for the ruptured sac to do, however. It breaks down and remains in the ovary, forming a yellow mass that is called the corpus luteum. The corpus luteum starts to manufacture a hormone of its own which is called progesterone, the function of progesterone being further to stimulate the uterine lining to form more glandular tissue so that it can support and care for a fetus if the egg that is ripening should become fertilized.

At this point, the ovaries begin a slowdown in the production of estrogen, the hormone that gives women a sense of well-being. In some women the withdrawal of the estrogen builds up a feeling of tension and irritability, or emotionalism, which is just the opposite of the "good" feeling a woman experiences at the beginning of her cycle and through ovulation. Many women patients have told me

FEMALE GENITALIA

INTERNAL

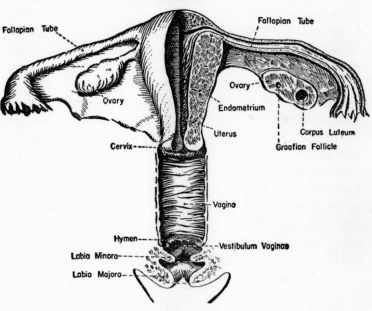

Fallopian Tube

Fallopian Tube

Ovary

Ovary

Endometrium

Corpus Luteum

Uterus

Graafian Follicle

Cervix

Vagina

Hymen

Vestibulum Vaginae

Labia Minora

Labia Majora

EXTERNAL

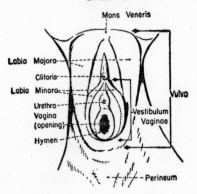

Mons Veneris

Labia Majora

Clitoris

Labia Minora

Vulva

Urethra

Vagina (opening)

Vestibulum Vaginae

Hymen

Perineum

about the "pre-menstrual week," when they are so "nervous they could jump out of their skins," and can't help being cross or moody. Medical research has established that when a woman's body is producing more progesterone than estrogen, her disposition is likely to be affected, and through no fault of her own.

In fact, the irritability and emotionalism from which many women suffer at menopause, the time when the ovaries cease their activity, are ascribed to lack of estrogen. The busy, well-balanced woman usually feels her bodily changes less than the woman who is generally nervous and high-strung. But the life of practically every woman is governed to a certain extent by her monthly cycle, as you will find after you are a married man and have been initiated into the feminine secrets.

If the egg does not become fertilized, it withers and passes out of the body through the vagina. Then the womb lining that was built up during the first part of the cycle begins to break down. The corpus luteum disintegrates and is absorbed. Finally, the discarded womb lining is sloughed away in the bloody discharge that we call menstruation (from the Latin *menstruus*, meaning *monthly*), because in normal women it occurs once in every lunar month. The average woman menstruates for about five days out of the twenty-eight of the lunar month, but some for only three days, and some for as many as six. When that is done with, the whole process starts over again!

Many peoples, including the ancient Hebrews, have considered that a woman was unclean when she was menstruating. You may remember Old Testament passages which describe the attitudes toward a woman "in her flowers," to use the poetic language of the King James Version. You may also remember that Rachel used menstruation to trick her father Laban, when she ran away with Jacob, taking her father's household gods with her. When the wrathful Laban caught up with them and searched their tents for his treasures, Rachel sank down on the chest that held the images and said she could not get up because "the custom of women is upon me." Laban went away empty-handed.

In some savage tribes today, menstruating women must hide away, for it is thought they will confer an evil spell upon any man who sees them. The truth is that menstrual blood is just like any other blood. A healthy, normal girl should feel no discomfort at this time, but unfortunately in this modern day a good many are more or less incapacitated for a day or two. Ovulation, during which the egg enters the Fallopian tube, and travels along it to the uterus, takes place about thirteen to seventeen days before the menstrual flow starts, and it is only during this time that the egg can become fertilized. The progress through the tube takes seven or eight days.

Fertilization, as I imagine you know, takes place when a sperm from the male, traveling up the Fallopian tube, encounters the ripened ovum on its way to the uterus. A fertilized egg will fasten itself to the wall of the uterus and remain there. In this case, the corpus luteum will continue in the ovary for several months, producing hormones which keep the womb from contracting and expelling the ovum. Other bodily changes incident to the development of a baby will swing into action.

It follows naturally that during pregnancy, menstruation will cease, for the rich womb lining is needed for the fetus. It usually does not begin again until several months after the birth of a baby.

You, of course, know that it takes about nine months for a baby to develop in the mother's womb, but even in this there are variations. When the infant is ready to be born, the muscles of the uterus begin to contract, gradually pushing the baby out into the birth canal. Slowly these rhythmical contractions propel the infant, usually in a state of indignation, into the outer world.

For the thirty or more years between the menarche, when menstruation begins, and the menopause, when it ceases, a human female goes through this cycle of secretion of estrogen, ovulation, secretion of progesterone, and finally menstruation, except during the periods when she is gestating an infant. It is easy to understand that women's lives are affected by this process in a way that those of men, who have no such phenomena, are not. This may not clear up all the contradictory behavior of your sister or your girl friend, but it may explain in part the reputation women have gained for being changeable.

A medical colleague once remarked to me, "You know, women have a pretty hard life. When a girl gets to be twelve or thirteen, she starts to menstruate and has to go through that every month. In her twenties, she gets married and starts to have babies. She has to go through childbirth, and be tied down by children. When she reaches the forties or fifties, she has to go through menopause, and has a miserable time. After she gets through with that, she can be pretty peaceful and comfortable the rest of her life—what there is of it."

Of course, for the normally constituted woman, there are compensations, and very great ones, for this pre-occupation that her body has with the reproductive processes. The normal, mature woman wants marriage and children above anything else in the world, and is willing to undergo any amount of inconvenience in return for the privilege of motherhood.

Women of intelligence and character have a strong impulse to keep themselves for men who will be the proud and loving fathers of their children. So far as the best type of woman is concerned, this is what sex is all about.

Glossary of Terms in Female Reproductive Processes

ANUS—outer opening of the rectum

AREOLA—brown circle surrounding the nipple

BIRTH CANAL—vagina

BREASTS—glands intended for the production of milk

CERVIX—lower end of the womb

CLITORIS—small erectile organ just above the opening of the urethra

CORPUS LUTEUM—yellow mass formed by the ruptured Graafian follicle, and producer of progesterone

EMBRYO—unborn infant in early stages

ENDOMETRIUM—lining of the womb

EROTIC—pertaining to sexual love

ESTROGEN—hormone manufactured by ovaries. Important in a woman's feeling of well-being

FALLOPIAN TUBE—connecting link between ovary and womb, through which the ripened egg passes after ovulation

FETUS—unborn baby from third month until birth

FUNDUS—upper part of womb

GESTATION—development of a baby in the womb

GRAAFIAN FOLLICLE—tiny sac, which contains an egg (ovum)

HYMEN—thin membrane near the opening of the vagina

LABIA MAJORA—outer lips of the vulva

LABIA MINORA—inner lips of the vulva

MENARCHE—time when a girl first menstruates

MENSTRUATION—bloody discharge, in which the discarded lining of the womb is washed away each month

MONS VENERIS—Mound of fatty tissue which is the upper part of the vulva

NIPPLE—erectile tissue at tip of breast, designed for baby to suckle milk through

OVARY—organ containing eggs (ova) and manufacturer of the important female hormones, estrogen and progesterone

OVUM—egg. The plural is ova

OVULATION—The process in which the ripened egg erupts from the ovary

PERINEUM—tissue between the vagina and the anus

PERIOD—in this connection, short for menstrual period

PROGESTERONE—hormone manufactured by the corpus luteum

URETHRA—outer opening from bladder, where urine is discharged

UTERUS—also called womb—pear-shaped organ in which the baby develops

VAGINA—passageway from the outside of the body to the uterus

VESTIBULUM VAGINAE—outer opening of vagina

VULVA—outer reproductive part in females

WOMB—see uterus

2. The Male Reproductive System

Compared with the female, the male reproductive organs, while more conspicuous outside the body, are nevertheless a rather simple mechanism. The penis, of course, is the organ for penetration of the female vagina, and the testicles make the sperm. It is rather interesting, however, that in the embryo, although sex was determined at the moment of conception, there is no discernible difference between a male and a female for several weeks. Before this time, each embryo has the same kind of gonads, or sex glands, which in the early stage of development are known as genital ridges.

It is after the eighth week that in the boy these genital ridges begin to grow into testicles, in the girl into ovaries. The external organs at first are merely a large swelling, which is called the genital tubercle. After about the sixth week of pre-natal life the genital tubercle of a male, and the fold of tissue that surrounds it, begin to take form as a penis, a scrotum (the bag holding the testicles) and a penile urethra, the tube for excreting urine which runs through the penis. And you might be interested to know that we men have a vestigial uterus, formed of the same material which makes the female uterus and vagina.

The boy baby at birth is provided on the outside of the body with a penis and scrotum, the latter containing the testicles. But since the testicles develop inside the abdomen and descend into the scrotum at a rather late period in the fetal life, a certain number of boys are born with undescended testicles. This condition may correct itself in time, but if it does not, should be corrected by surgery. For while a boy with undescended testicles may develop normally and become an apparently normal man, he will not as a rule be able to beget children, since the temperature inside the abdomen is too high to permit the sperm-producing cells to do their work.

The penis is largely composed of two spaces called the corpora cavernosa. These are made of a spongy tissue into which a great many blood vessels open. An erection comes about when the blood rushes into the spongy tissues, filling them so tightly that the whole organ expands, stands out from the body and becomes hard. A loose skin covers the penis, and the end of the skin is called the foreskin or prepuce. Sometimes the prepuce covers the end of the penis too tightly, in which case the doctor removes it in the slight operation called circumcision. While the entire penis has a rich nerve supply, the end of the penis is the most sensitive portion.

The testicles, lying behind and below the penis in their scrotum of corrugated skin, are egg-like in shape, about an inch thick and about one and three-quarters inches long. Like the ovaries, they are formed of two kinds of tissue. One type is responsible for manufacturing the sperm. The other type secrets a hormone, testosterone, which plays the same important role in the life and well-being of a man that estrogen plays in the life of a woman. It is believed to govern the secondary male characteristics—facial and body hair, deep voice, aggressiveness. Men who have been castrated in childhood by having their testicles removed have high, womanish voices and are beardless.

The testes—and incidentally, the same is true of the ovaries—are entirely separate from and independent of each other. One can be removed, and the other will carry on its task in procreation efficiently as long as it remains healthy.

The internal reproductive system of the boy at birth consists of the two vasa deferentia and the structures associated with them; of the urethra, and the prostate gland. The vas deferens is a muscular tube, whose purpose is to conduct the sperm from the testes up through the body in a horseshoe-shaped course to be stored in a small gland called the seminal vesicle, until it is needed; and when the time comes, to conduct it back down again to be ejected from the penis. As you will see by the sketch, one tube leads from each testicle through the inguinal canal into the abdominal cavity, and then on through the prostate gland. Here it empties into the urethra. Near the bladder it gets larger, and connects with the seminal vesicle. The seminal vesicle and the enlarged portions of the vasa deferentia act as the storehouse for the sperm during periods of sexual inactivity. The prostate gland is a muscular organ which, by contracting at the climax of intercourse, helps force the seminal fluid down the urethra and out the end of the penis. Both the seminal vesicle and the prostate gland secrete a fluid in which the sperms move and swim about.

Thus the urethra serves as the passageway for both urine and sperm. But Nature has provided a cunning little mechanism for keeping the two fluids from becoming mixed. Whenever semen is ejected, a little valve on the bladder closes automatically—one of the many wonders of the human body.

Women cannot conceive children after they have passed the menopause, usually happening in the late forties or early fifties. But strong, healthy men may beget offspring for twenty or more years after this time. In fact many authentic cases are on record of men who have begotten offspring when well past seventy years of age.

You probably know from personal experience that it is possible to have an erection during childhood. However, semen is not ejaculated then, and the penis does not become hard enough to penetrate a female vagina, except in those cases of glandular disorders where boys mature sexually at an abnormally early age. Normal boys may mature at anywhere from thirteen to fifteen, but on the average it is around fourteen that the testes begin to produce sperm, and erections followed by ejaculations of semen are possible. Semen is a white fluid composed of secretions from the testicles, the seminal vesicles and the prostate gland. Millions of spermatozoa swarm in normal semen—Nature is even more lavish here than in the production of eggs in the female.

Under the microscope, the sperm cells look very much like tadpoles, having flat heads, narrow necks and long, thread-like tails. They are extremely active, and when deposited in the vagina of the female, propel themselves by their long thin tails up through the uterus and into the Fallopian tubes. If an ovum has been expelled from the ovary and is lying in the tube, the sperm cells surround it and one of them penetrates the ovum, after which the ovum becomes impervious to other sperms. The lucky sperm, if I may so call it, then unites with the ovum, the tail drops off, and the new life begins at once through a process of cell division. It is believed that under favorable con-

MALE GENITALIA

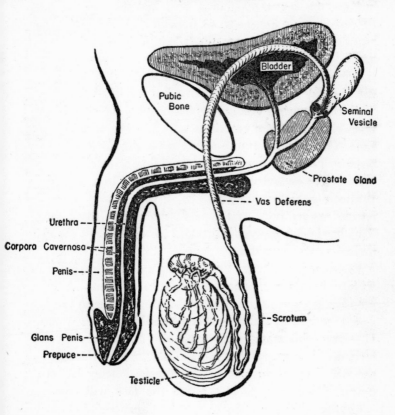

ditions, a sperm can live for about one day after it has been ejaculated.

Sometimes as a result of an accident or an illness such as mumps, the sperm-producing cells become damaged, and defective sperm are made, or none at all. The quality and number of a man's spermatozoa can be determined by examining a specimen of semen under a powerful microscope. It is possible in some cases through medication to improve the quantity and quality of sperm, but not in all.

At the moment, you are probably more interested in the phenomenon of the erections which occur from time to time in the healthy young male than in the matters just discussed. Nature's purpose in providing a mechanism for turning the ordinarily flaccid male organ into a hard instrument is easily guessed—it is so that it may enter the female vagina fully and deposit the sperm there safely. This hardening process is brought about through the sympathetic nervous system.

Prolonged, passionate love-making and intimate embraces with a female are practically certain to bring about an erection in a normal, healthy male. Boys and men can produce erections by dwelling on erotic subjects in their minds. However, this manifestation can also be entirely involuntary, and is not one that can be inhibited by the mind or the will. As in the case of the female, Nature has taken powerful measures to insure that the race will continue.

On the other hand, any man of intelligence and character can keep his passions in check. Even though he is sexually aroused and has an erection, civilized man can restrain himself from sexual activity which his mind tells him would be morally wrong, or disastrous in some way. In this respect the human male differs from his animal counterparts, who are driven by their natures to mate with any available female. Farther on in the book, I shall give some concrete suggestions for helping to control male passions and desires until the time has come to exercise them.

Glossary of Terms in Male Reproductive Process

CIRCUMCISION—cutting of skin at tip of penis, when it is too tight, or for religious or hygienic reasons

CORPORA CAVERNOSA—cavities of penis, into which blood rushes under sexual excitement

EJACULATION—expelling of semen from the penis

ERECTION—hardening of penis, due to rushing in of blood

GENITAL RIDGES—sex glands in the embryo

GENITAL TUBERCLE—swelling in an embryo which becomes the outer genital organs

GONADS—sex glands

INGUINAL CANAL—passage from testicle into body

INTERCOURSE—joining of male and female reproductive organs

INTERSTITIAL TISSUE—the part of the testicles responsible for manufacturing testosterone

PENIS—male organ for penetration of the female vagina

PREPUCE—skin covering end of penis

PROSTATE GLAND—organ which, by muscular contraction, ejects the semen at the climax of intercourse

SCROTUM—Bag which holds the testicles

SEMEN—liquid containing the spermatazoa

SEMINAL VESICLE—organ which stores sperm until they are needed

SEMINIFEROUS TISSUE—the part of the testicle responsible for manufacturing spermatazoa

SEXUAL ACT—intercourse

SPERM—short for spermatazoa (see below)

SPERMATAZOA—cells which fertilize the female ova

TESTICLE—egg-shaped organ below the penis which manufactures sperm and testosterone

TESTOSTERONE—male hormone which gives a sense of vigor and

well-being, and is thought to govern secondary male characteristics

URETHRA—tube which conducts urine from the bladder, and is
used for the passage of spermatazoa

VASA DEFERENTIA—tubes which conduct sperm from testicles
to seminal vesicle, and also help to store them

3. The Mating Act, and Reproduction in Other Forms of Life

Intercourse, or the act of mating, is the part of sex about which the veil of mystery is drawn. Human beings carry on the mating act in private, and those who have respect for themselves and for their partner are not likely to speak of it. Hence many boys get their first ideas about intercourse from those who do not respect either themselves or their partners and look upon it from an animal level. Conflicts and complexes arise when feelings of shame and disgust are associated with an act that is necessary and right, if the race is to continue.

As I said before, Nature intended the mating act to be highly pleasurable, and planned the male and female reproductive organs to make it so. Some persons in the past have considered it a sin to experience pleasure in intercourse, and until rather recently "nice" women were supposed merely to endure it. Now it is recognized that there is nothing wrong in the sex act itself; that when a man and woman are prepared to give a home and love to the children that may result, it is right and proper to obtain the highest satisfaction possible from the act of love.

We have seen that the female body has various areas, called erogenous zones, where nerve endings cluster thickly in order to arouse a woman sexually when these areas are caressed. The closer to the vulva, the more pleasurable these sensations become. Women do not ordinarily become sexually excited spontaneously, as men do. A woman's passions are aroused gradually through caressing of the erogenous zones by the man she loves. (I am speaking now of the normally sexed and self-respecting woman, the kind you will wish to marry.)

As a woman becomes sexually aroused, the glands about the vulva increase their secretion of fluid, lubricating the vestibulum vaginae to make easier the entrance of the male penis. Meanwhile the normal man becomes sexually aroused and has an erection. When both are ready for the penis to enter the vagina, the friction of the sensitive penile organ against the walls of the vagina, so richly endowed with nerve endings, becomes increasingly pleasurable for both. Presently the highly charged nerves of penis and vagina explode in a tremendous burst of sensation that is called an orgasm. With the male explosion, the semen is discharged, and the penis quickly becomes flaccid again. With the female, there are muscular contractions of the vagina.

You may possibly have heard vivid descriptions of the pleasures of intercourse with one girl or another from companions—I know that boys are likely to hear talk of this kind as they get older. But what the street-corner Lotharios cannot describe to you, because they are incapable of experiencing them, are the emotions surrounding the sex act when a fine man and a fine woman truly love and respect each other. During and after intercourse that grows out of love, there is an intensification of the tenderness, gentleness and consideration each partner already feels for the other. The birth of a child is the crowning miracle of such a mating, and redoubles the feeling of love and reverence that a mature, normal man feels for the woman he has chosen for his wife. The wife who is giving a child to a beloved husband feels the deepest satisfaction a woman can know. In this way, the sex act becomes a bond drawing husband and wife closer together, and through its attendant emotions constantly develops character and personality.

On the other hand, when the sex act is entered into merely for pleasures or to relieve sex pressures, without love or respect for the partner, the after-feeling is usually one of revulsion against the partner and of self-degradation. Why these things are so, we cannot say with authority. Some schools of thought maintain that it is because of guilt feelings, engendered by society's disapproval. But we know from as far back as records go that men have reacted in this way against "easy" women, who will give or sell themselves without love.

Sex carried out in a framework of love and protection for the partner, and cherishing the children who result, is the basis of our whole social structure—of homes, families, the will to achieve, the personal happiness that enables one to meet hardships and difficulties with equanimity. To learn how to find a worthy partner, and to be mature enough one's self to carry out the responsibilities of the adult male, while in the meantime avoiding mistakes that might endanger one's whole future happiness, should be the sex goal of the intelligent young person.

Animal Reproduction

While we are speaking of Nature's ingenuity in arranging the reproductive processes in man, I think it might be interesting to have a brief look at the way this matter is taken care of in other forms of life. As you know, in all but the most primitive organisms, two sexes are involved, but there seems no end to the variety of ways in which another generation can be brought into being.

People are inclined to hoot at mention of the "birds, bees and flowers," because so often they have been offered natural history in place of the information about sex in human beings which it is their right to have. Nevertheless, when you understand the human reproductive processes, it is fascinating to see how they compare with, or differ from, those of other species.

If you are ever near Cambridge, Massachusetts, I hope you will go to see the famous glass flowers at Harvard. Not only do these rank with the wonders of the world insofar as beauty and almost miraculous craftsmanship are concerned, they also show the many ways flowers, to speak of only one specie, have of getting themselves impregnated, and the cunning with which the flower parts are formed both to tempt insects inside them, and to be sure that the fertilizing pollen will be scraped off onto the female organs of the plant.

As for the bees, their reproductive habits are perhaps the most extraordinary and dramatic of those of all living creatures. You probably know that the Queen bee is the only one who has the ability to lay eggs, and that all by herself she will populate a hive of 50,000 or more. More amazingly still, she mates only once in her lifetime, and from this single mating will produce fertilized eggs for eight years or longer. Moreover, she can produce eggs from which will come future queens, or workers, or drones, which last is the not very complimentary name applied to the male bee. In ordinary times, this busy little Queen bee will lay around 300 eggs a day. But if the hive is depopulated by some catastrophe and workers are urgently needed, she can and will step her production up to 3,000 eggs a day.

Each season she lays just a few queen eggs, in specially built cells. Before sealing the cells, the nurse bees stock them with a special royal jelly, used only for the nurture of royal bee infants. Scientists have never been able to find out what this royal jelly is made of, but when it is fed to other animals, it increases their fertility. At such time as it becomes apparent that a new queen will not be needed this season, the Queen destroys her little princesses, for two queens in one hive might kill each other, and thus wipe out the whole hive. But if the hive gets too big, and the Queen realizes that she will have to lead a swarm to another place, she leaves behind her five or six of the royal larvae, of whom one will take her place in the old hive.

The first Queen bee to hatch out promptly kills her still-sleeping sisters. After that she spends a few days inspecting the hive, during which time her subjects stay at a respectful distance. Presently she feels that the time for mating has come, and she sings a special little song. Bee observers say that the whole hive hums with excitement when they hear the song, and the drones gather for the one big moment of their otherwise idle lives.

The new Queen goes to the entrance of the hive, and stands there for a short time. Then she unfurls the wings that she has never used before and launches herself straight up into the sky. Around a hundred drones tumble out of the hive after her. As the Queen flies higher and higher, the weaker drones drop out. The one who can stay the course—a bee-mating takes place a mile or more above ground—dies as soon as he has completed the mating act. Then the Queen returns to the hive, with twenty-five million or more sperm in her body upon which she can draw to fertilize her eggs as long as she lives.

Just as only enough queen eggs are laid each season to insure a new leader if the Queen Mother should die or depart, so only enough drone eggs are laid to make sure that there will always be one male strong enough to fertilize a new queen. The drones lead an enviably carefree life while it lasts. Their tongues are too short to gather honey, but they help themselves freely to the store brought in by the workers. With cold weather, however, there comes an end to their idyll. The bees have no intention of letting a bunch of useless drones eat up the community provisions during the winter months. The workers gently push the drones out of the hive, either to freeze or starve to death. Except for spider species whose ladies eat their mates as soon as the luckless males have impregnated them, this is perhaps Nature's most realistic example of the expendability of the sex that plays a minor part in the reproduction of life.

Reproduction in birds and animals has many points of resemblance with the human, some of which are amusing, and some rather embarrassing. For instance the male Manakins, small birds found in Panama, establish themselves in courting places. These little spots extend in regular lines for many yards through the forest, each courting place being anywhere from twenty-three to thirty-five feet distant from the next one. Several times a day throughout the mating season, the male birds come to their own special courting places and issue a call that can be heard from far off. The females apparently drop whatever they are doing and come. I am told that among young humans, this kind of technique is called curb service.

Most fish, as you know, reproduce in a hit-or-miss fashion. The females lay their eggs—some species return each season from far off to certain breeding grounds in order to do this—and the males swim about above the eggs, releasing a fluid called milt, which contains the sperm. The fertilized eggs and the young that hatch from them thereafter are on their own. But one variety, the stickleback, does it differently. The male carefully prepares a nest for the female to lay the eggs in. Then she is free to enjoy herself with whatever is the fish equivalent of women's clubs and bridge luncheons. The male stays home, and watches over the eggs and over the young after they appear. A few fish species are gestated inside the female, and the octopus has a reproductive method all its own. A special arm of the male hands the female a "packet" of sperm, placing it inside a special cavity in her, to us, repulsive body. As her eggs are laid, the sperm are released to fertilize them.

If the male plays a rather ignominious role in some forms of life, the bull seal restores his sex to its proper dignity and importance in the scheme of things by a performance that is as outstanding in its way as the Queen bee's is in its way. Every spring, the world's largest seal herd returns to its breeding grounds on the Pribilof Islands off Alaska, having spent the winter cruising about and never touching land. Each adult male addresses himself to the task of rounding up a harem, of from fifty to sixty females. The number depends upon two things: his powers of attraction for the opposite sex, and his prowess in fighting off the other males who would steal his ladies from him. Then the fun begins.

Each mature bull establishes himself with his harem in a "rookery" at the water's edge. No other seal dares come near the rookeries, nor does man, if he knows what is good for him. Each family head knows just who belongs in his harem, and fights any bull who attempts to encroach. If a female is detected stealing off toward another harem, her lord punishes her with death. But at the same time he has no scruples against luring some other bull's females into his harem, or accepting them if they come of their own accord. The female seal is one of the most graceful creatures there is, and looks demure in her—of course—genuine sealskin coat. But apparently her wifely loyalty is an extremely uncertain quantity, and in spite of the death penalty for unfaithfulness, the harem heads have to watch their ladies night and day. (A condition that also prevails in human harems, we are told.)

From reserved seats around the edge of the rookeries, the bulls who are maturing, but not quite ready to head a household, watch the harem proceedings with interest. If an older male shows signs of weakness, one of the near-adults will sail in, challenge his senior to a duel, and if victorious, will step into a ready-made harem. These are called "idle bulls," but the term is an injustice. They are idle only when compared with the mature bulls, who already head harems.

These last amazing creatures perform a feat of strength and endurance that is unequaled so far as I know. During the entire breeding season, from early April until late July, these gentlemen neither eat nor drink! The fact is that they are entirely too busy for such frivolities as this. One moment's relaxation, and their harem is gone.

At the beginning of the season, the bulls are so fat that their flesh quivers, but at the end, they are thin to the point of emaciation and scarred all over from the endless fighting. Their task done for the year, they drag themselves to remote corners of the island to catch up on their sleep. So exhausted are they in fact, and their sleep is so profound, that greenhorns often think they are dead. "A grotesque symbol of masculine vanity and truculence," is the unkind way one writer describes them. But these are the rules of seal society.

As you probably know, female dogs and monkeys menstruate as women do. However, unlike women, it is at their menstrual period that they can become pregnant. Some species of mammals have definite mating seasons. In others, the females have periods of "heat" which may occur at any time—cows, horses, dogs, for instance—during which their instincts drive them relentlessly to become impregnated.

You are well aware that the most fastidious, pampered, pedigreed female dog or cat, under the influence of this terrific sex drive, will mate with the first scruffy cur or alley Tom who comes along. When not in heat, the female animal will repulse the amorous advances of the male as fiercely as the most virtuous dowager.

Many birds and animals form into couples, and the male aids the female in protecting and caring for the offspring while they are helpless. There is no indication, however, that the parents feel any tie toward each other. Comes another mating season and they will pair off with other partners. Nor do they have any interest in the offspring after the youngsters are big enough to fend for themselves. The fierce mother love, which before that will make a female animal sacrifice her life for the young, vanishes entirely, and now she turns on them and drives them away.

It would be useless to deny that so far as our physical processes are concerned, and even in some of our social customs, we humans have many similarities to what we call the lower orders. But there are a number of ways in which we are different from them, and, this, too, is worth looking at.

Mankind alone of all living species is able to control his sex urges and desires. Thus he can make them serve him, instead of himself being the servant of his sex desires.

The normal man finds one woman, whom he loves, respects and reverences. With her alone can he find complete sex satisfaction, which involves all the best and finest emotions of which he is capable.

In mankind alone the sexual embrace is one of tenderness and gentleness, as well as of gratification of the senses. In fine sensitive men and women, the concern is more for the partner than for oneself.

In mankind the sexual embrace can be carried out with the lovers face to face, clasped in one another's arms.

Mankind alone feels a lifelong love and interest in the offspring.

I must admit that not all human beings live up to and realize all the foregoing ways in which we are set apart from the animal world. As we shall see presently, lack of intelligence, or distorted emotional lives, deprive many of their full human inheritance when it comes to sex. There are a certain number who approach sex from an animal basis. But these do so at a cost in humanity, and are to be pitied.

4. Growing Up Sexually

Anyone who studies the reproductive processes of animals as compared with those of man will be aware that what really sets us apart from them is one single factor—the capacity to love. We have seen that even the male animals who form a union with a female during the time offspring are gestated and reared, show no special interest in their mates. The animal mother who will fight to the death to protect her babies, wants no part of them after they have reached an age that would correspond in humans with adolescence.

The dream and desire for human beings is to attain sexual expression in a permanent love relationship with a member of the opposite sex. For men and women have a great need for love if they are to act like humans. This is not a sentimental statement, but a medical fact.

From time to time, doctors and criminologists encounter people who are incapable of feeling love. These unfortunates are not able to attach themselves emotionally to anyone, and they are likely to have defects of character, such as lying, selfishness and tendencies to steal. Furthermore, they lack remorse or any sense of responsibility for their acts. They are callous, inconsiderate and unconcerned about the feelings of others. These are the individuals who may, in a period of rage or violence, kill a kind friend or a member of their family.

Such persons, for want of a better name, are labeled psychopathic personalities. Although they may have some mental defect that partly accounts for their behavior, there seems no doubt that some of their tendencies are the result of lack of love in their infancy and early childhood, with the result that they in turn never have learned to respond with sincere affection for others.

Love in the true sense, therefore, is not something that happens to us like a bolt of lightning. The ability to love another person wholly and unselfishly is a matter of slow and gradual development. Our sexual natures develop, too, in the same slow, gradual way.

We think of children as not having sex natures, but this is not the case. Sex hormones are found in very young children. Perfectly normal youngsters go through quite definite phases of sex interest and sex activity of various kinds, and we know now that this is just as natural a part of their development as learning to walk and talk.

Unfortunately a great deal of harm has been done by lack of understanding of the fact that it is a normal part of growing up to have sex feelings and curiosity, and that children wouldn't be normal if they didn't. I find so many adolescents and adults plagued by guilt feelings over things they did as children which were perfectly normal and natural, that I think it will be worth while to trace the definite stages we all go through, both in growing into the capacity to love, and in becoming mature sexually.

The fact is that sexual education begins in early infancy, because the response of love begins at this time. The small baby smiles and gurgles as he is stroked, patted or petted.

When he is just a few months old, his eyes follow his
mother as she moves about. This is the foundation of affection, and of the tender feelings that will be so important
later on, when the child grows up, establishes a family and
has children of his own. It has been observed over and over
again that babies deprived of love and fondling will lan-
guish, no matter how well they are cared for in other ways.
Nowadays we supposedly hard-headed scientists rate love
as the most important single element in the rearing of a
child.

Children go through definite stages in the psychosexual
development, so called since it is a mingling of the physical
and emotional aspects of sex. During the first four years
of life, a youngster is getting acquainted with his whole
body and its processes, and this entire period is designated
as the auto-erotic (pleasurable interest in one's self).
Young children have no self-consciousness about their
bodies and it is normal for them to show interest in all
the parts, and those of other children, when they are dress-
ing and undressing together. They will examine another
child's navel or genitals, without any evidence of furtive-
ness. It is only when an adult shames them for their natural
curiosity that they develop ideas of guilt about their bodies,
and indulge in giggling and suggestive play. A little later,
the child of his own accord will copy the adult practice
of concealing his genitals, and once he is satisfied as to the
way he and his companions are made, his interest turns
to other things.

The stage following the auto-erotic is named the narcis-
sistic, after the mythological Greek boy who admired his
mirrored image so intensely that he finally turned into a
flower. The child's love quite normally and naturally is

turned toward himself. His whole philosophy seems to be "What a great boy am I!" and he is given to selfishness, boasting and showing off. (Girls go through this stage too. It isn't confined to our sex.) This isn't anything to worry about either, in the young child. It is simply an attempt on the part of the individual to find his own place in the world.

Around three or four, most children want to know where babies come from. And the way these first questions about sex are answered has a good deal to do with an individual's later attitudes toward reproduction. If adults are embarrassed or evasive, the child may stop asking questions because he fears loss of approval. Later on, he is likely to acquire inaccurate information from companions, which may so distort his ideas toward sex that he will be unable to accept it as a wholesome and happy aspect of the life of healthy adults.

The next stage in the psychosexual development is that around five, a boy usually gets a big crush on his mother—the first sign of a turning of love from self. Many five-year-old boys announce that they are "going to marry Mother" when they grow up. But while a boy will of course continue to love his mother, one who is developing normally will soon begin to be interested in, and fond of, persons outside his immediate family. At six it may very well be his teacher that the youngster plans to marry when he grows up, especially if she is a young, pretty teacher. And this is as it should be, for wonderful as a loving mother is in a boy's life, it is tragic if he remains so attached to her that he cannot fall in love with someone else when the time comes for that.

In their play, children of five and six may exhibit definite sexual urges. A boy in exceptional instances may make feeble attempts to insert his penis in a little girl's vagina. There is sometimes quite a lot of masturbation around six, evidence of sex stresses in the child's life.

Parents who do not understand the way children grow usually make a terrible fuss when such practices are discovered. One mother said to me, of her six-year-old son, "Am I going to have to keep him shut up, from now on, like a bull, in order to protect the little girls of the neighborhood from him?" I assured her that what she had to do was explain to him, quite calmly and lovingly, the facts of sex, and point out that there are better ways for boys and girls to play together.

When conduct of this kind is continued, quite often it is due to the fact that a child's curiosity has become morbid, maybe because parents shamed or punished when it was manifested. In my experience, boys who scribble obscene pictures and writings on walls are simply victims of poor sex education. I have known youngsters to become restless, tense and worried to the point of being unable to eat or sleep because their parents were so harsh about some of the natural manifestations we have been discussing. Some authorities believe that the seeds of sex perversion, where it exists, are planted in these early years, because as a child the individual was made to feel wicked, inferior and unhappy over the fact that he had a sexual nature. The effect of such treatment, as we shall see in a later chapter on the abnormalities of sex, is sometimes to fix a child emotionally in one or another of the psychosexual stages which otherwise he would have left behind him.

Up until the age of seven or eight, little boys and girls are pretty much alike in their body structure. Both are usually long and rangy, and both have tiny nipples on flat little chests. They play together on an equal basis, and fight and wrestle without any particular consciousness of sex. Soon after eight, however, differences begin to appear. First the boy grows heavier and taller than the girl, but she soon puts on a growth spurt of her own and outdistances him. By the age of ten-and-a-half, the average girl is heavier than the average boy, and soon she is taller as well.

Let's see what is going on here. First of all, the vital organs—the heart, the lungs and all the rest—are beginning to increase in size. This makes for the chubby torso which is characteristic of the pre-adolescent period. Between the ages of ten and fourteen, the organs inside the body—and this goes for the brain as well—grow from childish proportions to adult ones.

Next the glands swing into action. The male gonads or female gonads, as the case may be, start building the mechanism which will turn the boy into an adult male, the girl into an adult female. Toward the end of this period appear what we call the secondary sex characteristics. The girl's body assumes new curves, as her breasts begin to develop, and her pelvis grows wider. Hair begins to appear under the arms and on the mons Veneris. This is the stage of development known as puberty.

Inside the girl's body, the Graafian follicles begin to push toward the surface of the ovaries. By the time a girl is twelve or thirteen, she is likely to begin to menstruate. (Though some girls start this as early as nine, others not until they are eighteen.) However, the appearance of menstruation does not mean that a girl is now a mature woman. Biologists tell us that the maturing process goes on throughout the teens, and that a woman is not fully mature and ready for motherhood until she is in the twenties. Girls may have children during the teens, as we know, if they have intercourse. But they have an easier time in childbirth if they wait until they are fully matured, and the children are apt to be better specimens.

The boy normally begins his development at an age anywhere from a year and a half to two years after a girl starts hers. His skeleton becomes heavier, his shoulders broader, his muscles firmer. Downy hair appears on the face, and hair grows under the arms, perhaps on the torso, too, and around the sex organs. The pubic hair, as this last is called, is shaped like a V with the point downward in females, and like a V with the point upward in males.

His voice begins to change, and there is a period when he can't be quite sure what kind of sound is going to come out when he opens his mouth. This happens to every male, and there is no reason why a boy who is going through the voice-changing stage should be embarrassed about it. It is interesting that boy sopranos usually turn into baritones or bassos, and the boys who had lower voices in childhood become tenors after their voices have settled down.

The penis and testicles grow larger. Around fourteen, the average boy is likely to have nocturnal erections followed by ejaculation. It should be emphasized, however, that there is a considerable difference in the ages at which individual boys arrive at puberty, just as there is with girls. Boys who are slower to mature often worry because the penis and scrotum remain undeveloped, after their companions are more mature in this respect. In the great majority of cases, development takes place in due time. However, any boy who is troubled about it should consult his family physician. If by chance there should be some defect in the sexual mechanism, there is much that science can do today to correct it. If a boy still has an undescended testicle or testicles, it is a good idea to have this corrected at once.

Although physically speaking, a boy would be able to have intercourse and might beget a child at any time after seminal fluid is ejaculated, in all other respects he is not yet ready for this. His physical growth is not complete by any means. He is still dependent upon his parents, and must postpone sexual relations until he is mature enough emotionally and socially to live in co-operation with a woman, and to be responsible for a family.

The foregoing is the physical side of sex growth between the ages of ten and fourteen. On the psychosexual side, boys and girls go through a very interesting stage which is called the homosexual, but without the meaning that we attach to this word in the adult. There are adult men and women who don't get past this stage in their emotional development, and they are called homosexuals, because their love interest remains directed toward persons of their own sex. (Many people think this term is applied only to men, because they have the idea that it comes from the Latin word *homo* which means "man." The fact is that it comes from the Greek word *homo* which means "the same." It is therefore applied to women as well, when they are victims of this emotional ailment.) We all go through a period, between ten and fourteen, when we are more interested in our own sex than in the opposite one, but with the average person this is just one more phase.

Now the normal boy herds with boys, and the normal girl with girls. Boys form gangs, and go out seeking adventure. Or if they are fortunate enough to belong to the Boy Scouts or to similar groups, they delight in hikes and overnight camping and other activities of this nature. Up to this time, a boy may have enjoyed team games, but he wanted to be the star player. Now he would rather have his team win than be a hero himself. So strong is the feeling of loyalty a pre-adolescent boy has for a gang or group of which he is a member that he may be led into doing very reckless and even illegal things in order to gain the approval of his companions. Some boys get into serious trouble and are sent to reform school because of peccadilloes that a year or two later they wouldn't have dreamed of taking part in.

The adventurous spirit of this age is a fine thing, and so is the feeling of loyalty to the group or team we belong to. That is the way we learn to be members of a society. But a boy in this period would do well to repress wild and lawless impulses. It is just as much of an adventure to go exploring in the woods as it is to break into a vacant house, and no penalties are attached to becoming expert in woodcraft. A boy derives lasting pleasure and benefit from the skills he learns in a Boy Scout Troop or in the many activities furnished by a Y.M.C.A. In just a year or two the reckless impulses are outgrown. It is a great pity when they are allowed, at this early age, to wreck a life.

Girls do not as a rule behave as recklessly as many boys are inclined to do, but they form clubs of their own, and make a great point of scorning boys and having secrets from them. The average pre-adolescent considers love and romance as "mushy," and makes life miserable for victims of the tender passions. Boys can see no use whatever in girls, and girls return the compliment in full measure. But there's a big change ahead in this respect, as we shall see in the next chapter.

5. The Sex Side of Adolescence

In the preceding chapter it was mentioned that around thirteen the average girl may begin to menstruate, and around fourteen the average boy may begin to have erections followed by ejaculation of semen. When this point is reached, the stage is entered upon that we call adolescence.

By this time, the brain, heart and other vital organs will have reached adult size. The sex glands will be producing hormones on an adult or nearly adult scale. In a number of primitive societies, where very simple skills are sufficient for survival, young people are considered to be fully grown up when they either menstruate or produce semen, according to their sex.

Our own society, however, is a very complicated one, and this goes for relationships between men and women, as well as for making a living and for politics. A good deal of preparation is needed on many fronts if one is to be a successful adult in all respects. People don't change overnight from children to grown men. We therefore look upon adolescence as the last stage in the growing-up process, and a most important one.

For by the time a boy is twenty-one, he is considered ready to carry his responsibilities as a citizen of his country. By the end of adolescence, he supposedly should be in a position to break loose from his family, make a living, and marry and start a family of his own. Thus in our society, the teen years are devoted to getting ready for all the various duties and privileges that come with adulthood. In the meantime teen-agers remain under the control and supervision of their parents, and usually of schools as well.

It is not unnatural that there should be some confusion while a boy is adjusting to this new state of affairs. After he has matured sexually, he begins to feel independent and to want to run his own life. Yet he is still a minor in the eyes of the law and of his own family. Parents are usually prepared for their son's bodily maturing, but not for the aggressiveness which results from the outpouring of testosterone into the system. Boys often have sharp disagreements with their parents while both are trying to find out what this is all about.

In the old days, many boys used to run away from home at this stage, especially those whose fathers could not see any viewpoint but their own. Fortunately, there are fewer authoritative fathers now than there used to be, but there are still boys who leave home at fourteen or fifteen. Usually they live to regret that they also gave up the schooling that is so necessary today to prepare one for life.

For few boys are ready to tackle life on their own in a society like ours at the age of fourteen or fifteen. The wise young fellow will realize that while he needs the care and support of his parents, he also owes reasonable consideration for their wishes even though these may seem arbitrary at times. The day is not far off when he can be independent, provided he acquires the skills that will enable him to stand on his own feet. That is the thing to concentrate on.

Many boys are disturbed, and even alarmed, at the strong

sex feelings which come with the maturing of the sex glands and organs. This is especially likely to be the case if they have the impression that "nice" people don't have erotic impulses.

Nothing could be further from the truth. Every normal person is aware of sex feelings from time to time, and these are particularly strong in the young male. As we have seen, there will be erections at some time after you enter the teen years. This is quite likely to happen on awakening in the morning, because the bladder is full, the pressure causing the erection. The obvious remedy is to empty the bladder. Or it may occur during the day, as a result of sexual excitement, or spontaneously, with no apparent reason. A boy is apt to be considerably embarrassed, lest it show under his clothing.

It is simply a sign that you are developing normally. As the teen years go on, you learn to accept this phenomenon, and to fit it into its proper place in your life. Later on the very strong feelings subside somewhat. Meanwhile, you know that when the time comes, you will be able to play your role as a husband, and to beget children.

Rather interestingly, Plato, the old Greek philosopher, advised that a man should not marry and become a father until he was twenty-five, "when he has passed the point of life at which the pulse of life beats quickest." Normal girls have nothing to correspond with this terrific sex drive of the young male, and young girls do not understand it. Hence, many girls do not realize the temptations they place in the way of boys by conduct which to them is quite innocent. The teen-age boy, however, usually has the intelligence to govern his own impulses, and this is one of the important lessons he has to learn.

Some boys are upset by the nocturnal emissions which begin to take place in adolescence, thinking something is wrong with them. This is just Nature's way of relieving sex pressures in the male who is not yet ready for the responsibilities that are likely to arise from intercourse, or in the adult male who has no mate. Usually a nocturnal emission is accompanied by an erotic dream. You wake up to find that seminal fluid has been discharged. This is perfectly natural and normal, and is in fact a safety-valve Nature has arranged for us.

If a boy is inclined to be retiring, the effect of these new feelings and physical manifestations is sometimes to make him more self-conscious and shy. There is no reason why this should be the case. All normal males have the same feelings and reactions, and timidity will handicap a teen-ager in making the friends and indulging in the social activities that are an important part of growing up. On the other hand, if a boy is naturally robust, lively and aggressive, he may make himself obnoxious to girls by insisting on familiarities that they disapprove of and resent. This is another thing to guard against.

In the middle teen years, other things are going on in the body besides the glandular activity. It is now that a boy shoots up toward the sky. Some grow as much as six inches in a year. Arms and legs suddenly get long, and it takes the muscles a while to catch up with the new extensions. This is the reason why most teen-agers go through a period of awkwardness.

They may also feel languid, and be accused of laziness, while their bodies are making this tremendous growth spurt. On the other hand, some do not start this upward movement as soon as others. They are inclined to feel like pygmies surrounded by giants, and wonder if they are going to stay that way. I don't know which one feels more sensitive—the boy who towers above all his friends, or the one who has been left behind. By seventeen or eighteen, most boys have attained their adult size, though some may continue to grow after this. All the different body parts find their relationship to each other, and the period of greatest change, with its attendant worries and bewilderments, is over with.

Girls have their difficulties, too, in the early and middle teen-ages. Some are very embarrassed by the development of their breasts, and frightened at the appearance of menstruation, if this has not been explained to them properly. They have to adjust their lives to the new phenomenon, just as the males have to adjust to their own sex manifestations. But they have a compensation. Usually a girl "flowers out," around sixteen or seventeen—some earlier than this, and some later—into a loveliness of youth and freshness that is one of the most beautiful things on earth. As she grows taller, she loses her pre-adolescent chubbiness and acquires a trim figure. The most arrant tomboy is likely to become quite feminine, all of a sudden, and to be receptive to masculine attentions.

An excellent thing, for the adolescent, is entering the final psychosexual stage in growing up—interest in members of the opposite sex. This is called the heterosexual stage. Before adolescence, as we have seen, boys are inclined to be scornful of sentiment, and of girls. With sexual maturity, the normal boy finds himself with quite a different attitude. First he realizes that girls are rather interesting creatures, and is aware of them in a way that he was not before. Then one particular girl strikes his fancy, and he wants to be in her company as much as he can. He feels protective toward her, and toward girls in general. The special girl may change from time to time—in fact, that is the natural, normal thing during the teen years—but from then on womankind will occupy a big place in his life. Normal girls become aware of boys in the same way, and make themselves as attractive as they can.

This is exactly as it should be. Some parents are inclined to worry and to accuse a son of being "girl crazy," a daughter of being "boy crazy," when the telephone begins to show signs of breaking down under the strain. (I've watched six youngsters of my own through this period, so I know what it's like.) But the fact is that we should all be terribly worried if our youngsters didn't get interested in the opposite sex, or some member of it, during the teens. The final sex goal in growing up is to find a mate and have a family of one's own. Those unfortunate individuals who never manage the change from preoccupation with their own sex to preoccupation with the opposite sex do not grow up sexually, and are considered abnormal.

This doesn't mean that the normal boy will not continue to have friendships with members of his own sex. He will, and they mean a great deal to him. But when the impulse comes to form friendships with girls, too, my advice to you is to obey it. The teen-ager who grows up without the fun of mixed parties and without at least one girl friend is missing one of the vital experiences of the adolescent years.

With so many other changes taking place, it is quite natural that one's list of interests and activities will change too. In fact, they may keep changing throughout the teen years, and that is nothing to worry about either. Right now is the time when you acquire the knowledge and skills that will

fit you for adult life. Few of us know at this point what
work or profession we will go into when we are grown.
During these years, you are free to try out any number
of things, and in this way be able to find out what kind
of work you will like best, and where your greatest abilities are.

Many parents have told me they were worried because
John or Bill had dropped abruptly some interest that had
absorbed him before, and that they had thought was going
to be his vocation. Maybe it will be his vocation, but in
the meantime John or Bill is having a fling at something else.

It is probably a good thing that the adventurous streak
we spoke of in pre-adolescence gives way to more staid
and sober pursuits. At fourteen, a boy may go to almost
any lengths to pull off some spectacular Hallowe'en prank.
At fifteen, the same boy may not be interested in Hallow-
een at all, unless there is a dance or party where girls will
be present. This is typical of the change of interests during
the teen years.

I would say that it is proper to pursue any activity or
line of investigation that intrigues you, so long as it is a
legitimate one. It may be chemical experiments one year,
building radio sets another year, photography another year,
or playing the piano or drawing cartoons or tinkering with
a car, or tennis or golf or swimming or sharpshooting.
Whatever appeals to you in the teen years is worth a try.
The skills you pick up in this way may lead to a vocation
later on. If they don't, they will still be a source of pleasure
to you in later years. The day will come when you will
have to specialize in something. But the more activity
strings a man has to his bow, the wider his choice is in

selecting a vocation, and the more fun he gets out of life.

In the same way that interests and activities change, it is natural for companions and heroes to change too. Many boys take on a whole new set of friends when they enter senior high, and another whole new set when they enter college. The baseball hero of childhood may be replaced in your affections by an atomic scientist, and later on it may be some other individual entirely that you will take as your model.

Girl friends are likely to come and go in the same fashion. It is very seldom that a boy's first sweetheart is the girl he eventually marries, however wonderful he may think she is at the time. Some teen-agers have a whole succession of sweethearts before they find the one they feel is really it. This is not fickleness, but a sign that your interests are broadening. You can still be the most loyal of husbands to the girl who suits you in every respect.

One of the less desirable changes that sometimes takes place when the new interests, emotions and conflicts normal to the teen years take place, is a drop of interest in studies. Boys are particularly prone to this, and it has nothing to do with intellectual capacity. I have known many a teen-age boy with a high I.Q. to get bogged down, simply because he didn't study. Maybe he couldn't see any reason for plugging at Latin or geometry or Shakespeare. Maybe he would much rather take cars apart and put them together again. Or perhaps dates, or daydreaming, were allowed to interfere. Many a bright chap gets "washed out" in the first year at the college he had chosen, because he took too much advantage of his independence from home and parental authority. This is a great pity, when it stops a boy from completing the education he has planned, and that his parents are able and willing to give to him.

The connection here with sex may seem obscure, but it is real. It is sexual maturing that brings about the changed outlook, and here is another point where desires and emotions must be controlled for one's own good. The "big" interest during the teen years is usually temporary, whether it is a girl or an activity. In a year or two, it is likely to be another girl and another activity that engrosses you. You will wonder then why you ever let the first one divert you from your main course.

I remember vividly one boy who found high school endurable at all only because he played football. That was before the days of intelligence tests, but he seemed smart enough to do good work in his studies, and his parents were understandably annoyed when he got low grades even in the subjects he didn't actually flunk. He was always getting into jams, besides, and finally was expelled. His father came to me in despair. "What is the use of trying to get Jim back into school?" he wanted to know. "He drags along at the bottom of his class, he makes trouble, he doesn't care about anything but football. He'd like to get a job. Isn't it best to let him do that?"

I pointed out that in my opinion, Jim was just going through the teen-age doldrums, and given time would come out of them. "If he quits high school without finishing, the only jobs he can get are driving a delivery truck or working in a filling station. I don't think that is what Jim really wants to do with his life. Let's try to get the school people to give Jim another chance."

Among us we got Jim through high school, though it

wasn't easy. Then he decided he wanted to be a doctor—up to that time, Jim hadn't known what he wanted to be. Nobody had to urge him to enter a pre-medical course in college, and he started doing A work in all his subjects. When the coach urged him to go out for football, he refused, saying that his studies took all his time. This chap who had had to be dragged through high school by the hair of his head graduated from college a Phi Beta Kappa and was at the top of his class in the stiff medical school he attended.

I have seen this kind of thing happen time and time again, with boys who did stick with their schooling, even though they didn't see anything good or interesting in it, because they realized it was the only way to get where they wanted to go. After you reach the place where you know what work you want to do, it is a good feeling to find yourself in a position where you can get the preparation you will need to enter it.

It is a sign of maturity to do the job that you know must be done, for the sake of your future, whether you find it interesting or not. Schools today are better than they used to be about presenting the required material in a way that will make it have more meaning to realistically minded boys, I am happy to say. But, however yours is in this respect, always keep in mind that the job of the teen-ager is to open doors that lead to the things he wants in adult life. To finish school, whether it is high school or college, may seem a needless grind right now. In sober fact, though, it may mean the difference between becoming a mechanic or an engineer; between becoming a hospital orderly or becoming a doctor or a surgeon. A man's vocation determines to a considerable extent the kind of woman he can marry, and the kind of home he can have.

If you have the patience to stick with the training that is so necessary in these days, you will find that in time it will open the way to true independence, and to the kind of love life you will want.

6. Questions That Arise and Common Misconceptions

1. *What about masturbation? Does it cause insanity? Is it harmful in other ways?*

You probably know that masturbation is handling of one's sex organs, either to get relief from sex pressures, or for the pleasurable sensations that temporarily result. As we noted in Chapter 4, children go through periods when nearly all boys and many girls seem impelled to do a certain amount of this. These seem to be phases of normal psychosexual development, since so many youngsters have the same impulse at approximately the same ages. In addition, children who feel worried or unloved may have a tendency to masturbate, whether they are in a particular psychosexual stage or not.

The beginning of adolescence, when new, strong waves of sex feelings appear, is one of the periods in the psychosexual life when a tendency to masturbate is likely to occur. At this age, these episodes may be accompanied by fantasies of sexual intercourse. One of the very common emotional conflicts of adolescence arises because at times a boy thinks he can hardly help masturbating. Yet, conscious and unconscious memories from childhood make him feel that he is doing something wicked, and something that may harm him, may even cause him to go insane.

It used to be thought, indeed, that masturbation caused insanity. This misconception arose from the fact that insane people are inclined to lose their inhibitions, and may masturbate openly.

Now we know that if masturbation caused insanity, few people would be running around loose. However, a good many parents still tell their children that they will "go crazy" if they manipulate their genital organs. During adolescence, when the body shoots up and the arms and legs get long and awkward, a boy may feel that he is losing control of his body. The idea can easily be associated with fear of losing his mind, because he has done some masturbating. I find that many men carry lurking anxieties of this kind.

So far as masturbation itself is concerned, there is no medical evidence to indicate that an occasional indulgence of the type I have described harms, either physically or mentally. We encounter many types of neurotic disease which result from fears and guilt feelings about masturbation and other forms of childish sex activity, because parents have made a great fuss, branded a child as wicked and made sex expression of any kind seem horrid and wrong. But this is because the parents did not understand the normal growth and development of children. So I would say that a person who has at some time yielded to this inclination need not feel that he is branded with shame, or that he has suffered physical hurt.

However, it is abnormal to be constantly preoccupied with one's own body, and the sensual gratification one can obtain from it. I have seen some boys who fall back on masturbation as a compensation for feeling inferior and inadequate. To use masturbation in this way may be a severe handicap in becoming mature.

It is not strange that in the teen years, one should often feel inferior and inadequate. I imagine most of us do at times. A teen-ager is confronted with a great many new challenges, all at once. School work gets much harder. So does competition in sports and other activities in which a normal boy would like to excel. The normal teen-ager would like to be popular with girls, and may feel like a social outcast if the girls he chooses do not warm up to his advances, and if he is left out of parties. Often parents do not understand the new ideas and ways that come with adolescence, and constantly criticize. On top of this, a boy's own body is acting in strange and sometimes embarrassing ways. Only a superman could take all these things in stride, and not be discouraged now and then.

The way to overcome inadequacy is to keep trying. Everyone has failures in learning new things, whether it is study or sports or getting along with girls, and it is from our failures that we learn the most. Whatever your particular problem may be, make an aggressive attack on it, and keep working at it.

If you are lonely, hunt up somebody else who is lonely —there is always someone around. If it's studies, keep plugging. Don't let yourself float off into sexual indulgence. Working on your problem is bound to get you somewhere. A habit of masturbation will get you nowhere.

If a boy has an inordinate desire to masturbate and feels incapable of making an aggressive attack on the emotional or social problems that worry him, he should by all means talk the matter over frankly with his family physician. No up-to-date man of science is going to be shocked, and he most often is helpful in counseling about the emotional problems which bring about the abnormal desire to masturbate, or in suggesting an expert who can do so.

2. *Are frequent nocturnal emissions harmful?*

It is not abnormal for the adolescent boy to have what are known as nocturnal emissions from time to time. However, when they occur too frequently, that is, several times a week, it may indicate that he is being overstimulated sexually and has too much of his interests centered on sexual matters and too little on the normal activities of the teenager. Even if they occur too frequently these emissions do not have any damaging physical effects. Now and then frequent nocturnal emissions may mean that there is some type of physical disorder present which is causing irritation of parts of the genital system. In such instances a visit to the physician is important so that the abnormal condition may be corrected. In any event the occasional emptying of the seminal vesicles which may occur at the end of an erotic dream is no cause for concern.

3. *Erotic thoughts and urges*

One of the plagues of the teen-ager who does not know what is going on inside his own body mechanism is an upsurge of erotic thoughts. The boy who wants to be as clean in mind as he is in body may sometimes feel that he is obsessed by lewd devils, which he cannot fight off no matter how hard he tries.

This too is a normal part of the development to maturity. The activity of the sex glands brings about urges to do something about sex. Moreover, boys are now aware of the sexual relations between men and women, and are naturally curious about them. They are constantly seeing new meanings in what before had been taken as a matter of course. The relations of men and women have occupied the minds of writers, artists and just everyday people ever since the beginning of time. It is no wonder that this vast new subject should occupy a place in the mind of an adolescent who is going to be an adult before very long. And it is an important part of education, too, to get some understanding and realization of what goes on between the sexes before one is called upon to fill a sex role.

Probably it is impossible to bar all such thoughts from your mind, and you will find that as you grow toward adulthood and have natural and wholesome relationships with girls, these involuntary fantasies will recede. But since the teen-ager is not in a position to carry out sex fantasies, it is a good idea to fill your mind with other interests and pursuits, which will leave small time for erotic imaginings.

4. *Curiosity about the female*

Interest in the female figure is a very natural part of being a male. I would feel sorry for a man who didn't get pleasure from the sight of a trim feminine figure and a delicately turned ankle. I would consider it a sign that his sex glands had stopped working, and that he is no longer a man in the male sense. Women work so hard to get or to keep nice figures that we may conclude they are not averse to giving men innocent pleasure in this respect.

Every adolescent, on his way to becoming a grownup, has a right to know something about the opposite sex. I have explained the female sex organs to you in detail because I feel that so strongly. There is nothing wrong in learning of the general body structure of women by looking at statues or paintings of nudes. There is nothing wrong, in fact, with the nude human body, and familiarity with it enables an artist to view it as an object of esthetic appreciation, a doctor as flesh that needs his ministrations, both without any lascivious feelings.

Prurient curiosity, however, is something again. It is immature to drool over deliberately lascivious pictures—human beings behaving like beasts are disgusting to the sexually well-adjusted person. And no self-respecting girl or woman enjoys the feeling that a man is mentally undressing her. The nice girl likes to be approached as a pleasant, interesting human being. A frank, esthetic appreciation of her beauty is always acceptable, but a sexual appraisal is revolting to a girl who has something besides her body to offer a man.

There are girls and women, I know, who deliberately accentuate the sexual parts of their bodies. The built-up bras that you see advertised, the dresses that are designed to call attention to breasts and hips, the bathing suits that seem planned not so much to cover, as to intrigue curiosity about the parts that are covered—what shall we say about these things?

I can assure you that many young girls, when their mothers let them dress in a way that flaunts their femaleness, aren't aware of the reactions it may produce in males. As I said in Chapter 5, the average young girl hasn't the slightest conception of the male sex drive, and the involuntary reactions of the young male to sexual exhibitions. When a girl reaches the heterosexual stage, she has a normal and natural desire to be attractive to boys. Many copy the dress and ways of movie sirens, because these ladies seem to attract men in droves. Most teen-age girls would be shocked and horrified if they realized that their innocent desire to have nice attentions from the male were being misconstrued. We men just have to figure that they know not what they do, and make allowances.

There are girls and women, however, who know exactly what they are doing, and do it deliberately. If you have reason to feel that certain ones dress and act as they do for the express purpose of rousing male passions, it is well to avoid them. A girl or woman who knowingly extends an open invitation to all males is unlikely to be a satisfactory friend or companion for one male.

5. Is sexual frustration ruinous to personality?

Nowadays we hear a good deal about the harmful effects of sexual frustration—that is, refraining from sexual expression through intercourse. The Freudian school traces all manner of personality difficulties and even bodily illnesses to this. And it is quite true that to consider sex wrong and bad, and to try to root out sex feelings from one's life by denying that they should exist, is likely to lead to anxious feelings and in time to physical symptoms which have no organic basis.

With all that has been said and written about sexual frustration, I don't wonder that many teen-agers get the idea that they will suffer some kind of physical harm if they do not have intercourse, for few writers nowadays take the trouble to point out that indulging in illicit sex may bring about situations and consequences that are just as harmful, or even more harmful, in other ways.

So let us examine this proposition. In the first place, I don't think it can be said too often that a normal sex life is an important part of one's personal happiness and fulfillment in adulthood, and is something to work toward. This does not mean that there are not many men and women who lead celibate lives and who are nevertheless well-adjusted useful adults. These people have learned to keep their sexual desires under control and to work them out in constructive activities.

Let us remember that many vigorous, normal adults are compelled by circumstances to do without sexual expression for long periods of time—as when a husband and wife have to be apart from each other, for instance. Many lead celibate lives for religious reasons. It does not hurt them, if they have a wholesome attitude toward sex, and use their energies in constructive avenues.

In our society, the teen-ager as a rule is not ready for the possible consequences that must be taken into account if one has sexual intercourse. The average girl is not yet ready to become a mother. The average boy is not yet ready to maintain a home and support a family. When parenthood comes before one is ready to carry its burdens and responsibility, believe me, it can have a serious effect on all the personalities involved.

It is well known today that sex impulses can be expressed in substitute ways—in creative work and social activities—until the time comes when a youth or an adult can satisfy his intimate needs in a manner that is socially acceptable, and does not bring with it feelings of guilt and shame and remorse. This is called sublimation.

The wise, well-adjusted teen-ager will accept cheerfully the limitations put on his sex life, for he will realize that there are excellent reasons for them. He can look forward hopefully to full and satisfying sex expression at such time as he is prepared to be responsible for a wife and children. In the meantime, he uses his energies to speed that happy day. He busies himself with studies which prepare him for a future trade or vocation. Librarians are ready to make him familiar with a world of fascinating literature and knowledge. He establishes warm, friendly relationships, based upon common interests and problems. He finds wholesome expression for his vim and vigor in hobbies, athletics, music, parties, dancing, dramatics and a host of other things. People busy with occupations they enjoy seldom suffer from frustration. When teen-agers suffer, it is usually because they aren't taking a full enough advantage of all the many things it is possible for them to enjoy.

6. *Is it a proof of manhood and virility to make sexual conquests?*

You will invariably meet males—maybe you know some now—who will boast of their prowess in seduction. It is not the particular girl they are interested in, but seeing whether or not they can add her to their list of conquests. Once this has been attained, they care nothing about the consequences of their conduct to her, and start another chase. Any decent man hates to see a girl he likes get mixed up with a "wolf" of this kind, for he knows that all the protestations of love and interest are just a line, and that there is nothing ahead for the girl but unhappiness.

Such men are not driven by excess virility, but by a deep-seated fear that they are lacking in virility. That is why they have to keep proving over and over to themselves that they are able to seduce a fresh victim. The man who has a secure knowledge of his own virility does not need constant proof that he is able to play a manly role. It is normal in the teens to be attracted to different girls from time to time, but the normal teen-ager likes the girls for themselves, he doesn't feel it necessary to seduce them in order to build up his own ego. The "wolf" who goes from one sexual conquest to another is an emotionally sick person, who should seek psychiatric help.

7. What about the "double standard" in morals?

Until quite recently, a girl was subjected to all manner of shame and degradation if she lost her virginity before marriage, but it was generally assumed that a man would have had sexual experience. It does not help matters when women assert the same privileges, as they have done at different times in the world's history. The moral laws have excellent reasons behind them, as you will realize when you have daughters of your own and think what might happen to them if they claimed the same sex freedom that men have traditionally enjoyed.

It is simply fair play to treat girls in the same way that you would want other men to treat your own womenfolk. Would you like some other chap to behave with your sister in the way that you behave with your girl friends? That is a pretty good criterion to follow. Many intelligent girls and women despise the hypocrisy of one standard for men and another for women ("double standard"), and they have every right to. They respect a boy or man who carries out himself the standards he sets up for other people. What is right for one sex when it comes to morals is just as right for the other, and it is just as much the responsibility of the male to keep boy and girl relationships on the right basis as of the female.

7. Boy and Girl Relations as They Should Be

Having disposed, as I hope, of some of the questions and misconceptions that arise after a boy has developed sexually, let's look now at the working out of the attraction the normal boy will begin to feel toward the opposite sex. Let's remember that at this point, the purpose is not to find a lifetime mate, but to get on as easy and natural a footing with girls as with boys. Some boys feel very shy about this, and some men remain shy with women as long as they live. They lose a great deal of the joy of life when this is so. Quite apart from the sex factor, one of the great pleasures of maturity is the mingling of men and women on a social basis. The man who gets tongue-tied every time he finds himself in the presence of an attractive woman is obviously at a considerable disadvantage.

Girls usually are ready to help by making themselves look as well as they can, and by getting up parties to which boys are invited. Some offer encouragement in the way of flirtatious glances, or by making the first overtures in starting a conversation. Many girls, however, are too shy to do these things.

That doesn't matter particularly. The male is supposed to be the aggressor, and a boy has the privilege of making overtures to any girl who appeals to him. To be sure, he risks some rebuffs, but his pride need not suffer. There are plenty of other girls to whom he can address himself if one or two turn him down. On the other hand, the girl is supposed to wait to be asked, and if she makes advances which are rebuffed, her pride suffers a good deal. The boys have all the best of it in this particular deal, and no young male should hesitate to take advantage of his masculine prerogatives here. I know college men who brood over the fact that they lack girl friends when all they need to do is to take a telephone and start calling numbers! Men have only themselves to blame when they lack feminine society. If they hang back bashfully and wait for girls to make all the overtures, they aren't very manly men.

It isn't even necessary to start out with anything as portentous as a date. If you just go up to a girl after class and discuss with her some point that came up in the course of the lesson, or walk home with her, or sit by her in the assembly hall, it starts the ball rolling. From associations like these, opportunities will arise to suggest some activity or entertainment she might enjoy.

When boys don't feel too sure of their personal attractions, it is sometimes easier to get up a group project. "You girls bring the food, we boys will furnish the transportation, and we'll all have a picnic." This sort of thing could well be part of the life of every teen-ager.

There is nothing like association with girls to knock off our rough masculine corners. As I have already mentioned, boys go through a period of adventurousness before they mature sexually. It is also a kind of roughneck period with the average boy. He hates to wash and to get dressed up. He is often loud and boisterous. This is all right in the pre-adolescent stage, but some men never get past it. The normal boy wants to be acceptable in polite society when he grows up. He would like to know the things a gentleman is supposed to do, and how to do them. Association with girls, attending parties, being in other homes and observing how older, more experienced people do things, is the way he gets the preparation he needs for this role, too.

Don't hang back from association with girls because you are not up on your Emily Post, or stay away from formal occasions because you don't know the ropes. I don't think I have ever attended a formal dinner where everybody used exactly the right fork or spoon on every occasion, and I am sure nobody cared. When you are confronted with a new social experience, don't hesitate to ask somebody how you should proceed. Keep your eyes open to see how other people are conducting themselves, and next time you will be a veteran yourself. If you are genuinely thoughtful and considerate of the people about you, it won't matter if you don't know all the formal gestures to begin with.

If you make a girl feel that you are alert to her comfort and ready to protect her from any unpleasantness, you are a gentleman in the true sense. Of course, that applies to protecting her from an unpleasant experience with yourself as well as with outsiders.

The very best manners of all, and the things most appreciated by the feminine sex, are those you do spontaneously out of kindly impulses. Teen-age boys can be very cruel, without realizing it. A chap may be asked by his hostess to take to a party a girl whom he considers a "drip." I have known some boys in such cases to behave in a surly manner, dump the girl at the party and then disappear until it is time to take her home. A shy, retiring girl may acquire an inferiority complex from an experience like this that it will take her years to get over. Thoughtless males cluster around the most popular girls, and leave the others on the sidelines. It is excruciating agony for a girl to find herself a wall flower. If you are responsible for a girl on any occasion, it is your job as a gentleman to see to it that she has as nice a time as you can manage. If you see a girl being left out, it isn't going to cost you anything to ask her to dance, or to sit down by her and talk with her for a while.

Trying to see that other people have a good time as well as yourself is the mature reaction to social situations. Discerning girls chalk up a high mark for boys who display this quality. A beautiful, brilliant girl I know surprised her friends by choosing as a husband the least "eligible" young man among her many suitors. That is to say, the others were better looking, had more money and were "smoother" than he was. Her mother told me it was because the girl had observed that Hal was always so nice to people that the more glittering young men considered beneath their notice. She felt this showed a character and a kindliness in Hal that were what she wanted in a husband.

I am always sorry when a boy holds back from feminine companionship because of shabby clothing and lack of pocket money, for with the right kind of girl, it is what you are, and not what you have, that is important. If you are scrupulously clean yourself—which goes for fingernails, too—and your clothes are clean and look as well as you can get them to, no one worth having as a friend is going to care if your wrists stick out beyond your coat sleeves and your trousers are mended.

The right kind of girl won't expect the sort of entertainment you are unable to afford, and it is proper to be perfectly frank about this. Girls do like attentions, and you should use your gray matter to find ways of providing them. But if a girl is truly worth while, and knows, for instance, that you are working your way through school or have to turn your earnings in to the family exchequer, she will be as pleased with a corsage from your mother's garden or a bunch of violets from the woods, as with an orchid.

Boys complain a good deal because dating is so expensive, but I usually find that they are trying to date the glamor girls who build up their own egos by demanding expensive attentions. I understand that some girls of this kind know to the penny what a boy friend's allowance is and plan so that it is all spent on them! Why bother about girls of this type? There are any number of lovely girls, probably quieter ones, who will be much more rewarding companions intellectually, and who will understand and sympathize with a teen-age boy friend's financial situation. The parents of a girl like that are usually of the same kind and admire a boy who is trying to work his way up in the world.

People who judge others by money standards simply stamp themselves as immature, superficial persons whose friendship would not be worth while even if you had it. The snobbish "upper crust" that one finds in nearly every high school or college often is not heard from in later life. Since I worked my own way through school, and a good deal of the time any rag man would have refused the clothes I had to wear, I take a lot of pleasure in a story I once heard. It was about a girl who was ordered by her sorority sisters to stop dating a young man who was working his way through college by delivering milk. It hurt their standing, they thought. (I know that in many places there are such stupid rules, as for instance that a fraternity man may not date a girl who doesn't belong to a sorority.) The girl refused to obey and was dropped from the sorority. Many years later the girl, then Mrs. Herbert Hoover, wife of a fine President of the United States, was offered an honor by her erstwhile sorority. She is said to have replied that she was sorry, but she was unable to accept it. "You see," her letter read, "I married the milk man!"

An intelligent, clean, well-mannered, ambitious boy has the world before him. There is no worthwhile girl, no worthwhile company, that he may not aspire to.

A question I am often asked is at what age dating should begin. My reply always is that the time to start is whenever a boy feels the urge, and has found a girl who strikes his fancy. You needn't worry if you don't get the urge at precisely the same time your companions do. Maybe you are younger than they are, or maybe your development to maturity is a little slower than theirs. It's a good idea to do something about the urge when you feel it, though. Some boys squelch it down, and then lose confidence in themselves. It may be years before they finally break through into happy heterosexual relationships.

Once you have made the plunge, it doesn't mean that you have to make dates and parties your main business in life, however desirable a certain amount of this kind of thing may be. In the early teens, a little of it usually goes a long way. Working into boy and girl friendships too, is generally a slow and gradual matter. And besides, a teen-age boy has a number of other important things to do, which he mustn't neglect. Attaining a feeling of ease in social situations, so that they hold no terrors for you, is the principal thing. It is much more painful to acquire if you wait till you are in the twenties or older. But once you have attained it, you may go for long periods without dates and without wanting to date, and be perfectly normal.

Many boys don't settle down to any one girl for quite a long time. They may ask various ones that they know to parties, or to the movies, or to sports events; they become the "second man" on a double date. It may be a long time before any one girl "gets under your skin," but if you are on a companionable basis with girls and can hold your own in a mixed group, you needn't feel that you are peculiar.

Any form of wholesome entertainment that both boys and girls enjoy is proper for the teen-ager. Since I am a doctor and a health officer, I only hope that your group doesn't carry on until far into night. As I have said before, most boys and girls continue to grow throughout most of the teen years, and while they are growing, they need lots to eat and plenty of sleep. During this period they are also busy and active with studies and a host of other things. The heterosexual adjustment can and should be managed without loss of health, from too late hours, and without the sacrifice of other important factors in development. If your parents or teachers urge you to keep a proper balance between the play and work aspects of life, they are doing you a service.

A second point that comes up often nowadays in teen-age dating is "going steady." I'm told that this practice has arisen largely because girls like to be sure of an escort, which is understandable, but "going steady" too early in your heterosexual life may defeat one of the main opportunities of the teen years. That is to get to know a number of members of the opposite sex rather well, so that you will have a better idea of the opposite sex in general, and a better idea of the kind of girl you will want to settle down with eventually.

As I have said before, it is natural in the teen years, though not always essential, for interest in one girl to wane, and interest to turn to another girl as one's own interests broaden and change. The same thing quite normally happens with girls. If your girl friend gets more interested in another chap, that is her privilege and you shouldn't have any hard feelings about it. In the same way, it should be your privilege to change off now and then. If a girl becomes possessive, you can be kind and gentlemanly, but you should firmly resist getting tied down to one girl before you feel ready for this step. The great thing about the teen period is the freedom you have to experiment with different things, and to know different kinds of people. You shouldn't give up this freedom unless you feel definitely that you have found what you really want and this usually takes time. In that case, of course, it would be foolish to change. But boys and girls who "go steady" simply because it has become a habit and they would have to face scenes if they broke it off, are cheating themselves of part of the benefit they should get from teen-age dating.

Early in your dating career you may find a girl who attracts you very much, and she may return your feeling in full measure. "Is this love?" you wonder. It is always a kind of love when you feel an outpouring of emotion toward another person, when you want to be with that person all the time you can, and would do anything in the world for her happiness and well-being. To feel an emotion of this kind for a girl proves that you have the capacity for the unselfish love that is such an important part of being mature. It's a fine thing, a wonderful thing.

But whether or not it is the love of a lifetime is something else altogether. The period of adolescence is a period of romantic urges. Many feel an awakened interest in poetry, in art, in music, in beauty of all kinds. There is a tendency to idealize the girl of the moment, to endow her with all the qualities of the romantic heroines. We call this, "being in love with love." But presently you may find that what you were in love with was not the actual girl herself, but a mythical creature you had built up in your own imagination. You needn't feel cynical or embittered if your goddess turns out to be human after all, and this shouldn't make you distrustful of love. Such an experience is part of your education in learning to know yourself and in learning to know women.

The great point in teen-age love affairs is to avoid behavior, under the stress of what you have taken to be love, that may be irrevocable in its effects. Throughout the whole period from fourteen to twenty-one, it is not impossible that each year you will be quite a different person from what you were a year before, with an entirely new set of tastes and desires and interests. You may carry some of your present interests and friendships through life, but right now no one can say which ones they will be. I have known juniors in college to drop a vocational interest they had held steadily up to that point and go in for something as different as night is from day. It is very possible that the girl who answers all your dreams and desires right now may not do that when you are twenty-one. This would be nothing against the girl, or against you either.

It is, therefore, just good sense to put limitations on expressions of affection during the teen years. Because they know that love is essential to sex expression on the right basis, some boys and girls get the idea that love is a reason and excuse for sexual expression, at whatever age and in whatever situation they may be.

This is a fallacy that has led many a well-meaning pair into sorrow and difficulty. The loves of the teen years are as sweet and beautiful as any love. But they shouldn't be taken too seriously, for there is every likelihood that they will change. There should be nothing in the relationship that will make it hard or dishonorable to change.

Kisses, when they arise from genuine regard and affection, caresses that do not involve the intimate parts of a girl's body, are a proper expression of love. They do no harm and leave no scars. A man can look back with pleasure as long as he lives upon an idyllic teen-age affair, which left the girl as sweet and innocent as she was when he first knew her. He will have a feeling of affection and gratitude toward her, because he experienced with her the sweetness and beauty and poetry of early romance, without the bitter after-taste that a man has when he has done things he knew he shouldn't with a girl or woman he no longer cares for. And this is not to mention the more tragic consequences which we will talk about in a later chapter.

It is just good sense to play down the physical side of a teen-age relationship and to play up the feature of companionship in activities you both enjoy—activities which will help both of you to develop your talents and skills and abilities in various lines. If you haven't any common interest except to make love, it's a danger signal, and you would do well to heed it.

Most parents want their sons and daughters to have a good time and to develop normally during the adolescent years. However, they are sometimes worried over dating and young love affairs for fear the sex impulses may get the upper hand and lead to intercourse, with its possible consequences, before a young couple are ready to assume these consequences. This is not peculiar to young love, but a thing that may happen to lovers of any age if they are not on guard against it. It is part of the parents' job to protect the boys and girls for whom they are responsible from experiences that may be lastingly harmful. You mustn't blame them if they try to do this, so long as they do not frown upon all association with the opposite sex.

Parents of young girls are only doing their duty when they make some inquiries as to the character of the boy their daughter is going out with, forbid the daughters to go to places of doubtful reputation, and establish an hour to get home after a date or an entertainment. This is in reality a help to the boys and girls themselves, in the first flush of young love or of sex attraction, to keep things from going farther than either one intends. When you have a daughter of your own, you will safeguard her in this same way.

If a young man is understanding of the genuine parental love and concern which prompt such restrictions as these and complies with them cheerfully; if he shows himself to be responsible and manly in looking out for a girl's welfare, the parental fears and worries will disappear.

No boy or girl need be ashamed of an attraction toward the opposite sex, and no informed, emotionally stable adult will be anything but pleased when boys and girls have a wholesome good time together. Since you are better off yourself when you keep it that way, this is a point on which there should be no quarrel between the older and the younger generations.

8. Why Sex Must Be Controlled

Right here I can see a question forming in the minds of some of my readers. It might go something like this:

"But, Dr. Bundesen, you have talked at considerable length about sex as a normal and natural part of life. You have described the phases children go through, and implied that people shouldn't be shocked or disturbed if they give expression to their sex feelings. Then you talked about the strong sex feelings that come with sexual maturity, and you even mentioned that Nature is urging us to 'do something about them.' Yet when it comes to this last point, you tell us we shouldn't. Isn't that illogical? If Nature intends for us to have full sex expression after we reach the stage where this is possible, aren't we going against Nature if we deny ourselves the outlet she seems to have had in mind?"

The answer to that is frankly that in some ways, and under certain conditions, we are. In a civilized society, we deny our natural, primitive urges in quite a lot of ways. When a cave man became angry, he grabbed a stone or club and did his best to kill his enemy—and probably every other adult man he saw was an enemy. If we still lived by ourselves in caves and dens, as mankind did in the beginning, we could continue to carry out our primitive urges. We'd be very likely to get slapped over the head as a result of somebody else's primitive urges, but that would all be part of the game.

When we live together in groups, however, one of the first things we have to learn is to suppress primitive urges. Rules are made by the group for the benefit of all. As we grow up, we learn to exercise sufficient control over our desires and feelings to abide by these rules.

Control of sexual reactions is no more difficult than the many other controls that people have to learn from earliest childhood. The two-year-old learns to control his bowel and bladder functions. It is a part of growing up to suppress the primitive urge to urinate or defecate wherever one may be. When he is a little older he learns not to eat with his fingers or to pick his nose or to grab another child's playthings. Parents are compelled to impose many curbs on primitive impulses for their child's protection, and also to train him to live with a group and be accepted by it.

When it comes to the expression of sexual feelings, there is one very great difference between the kind of expression that is possible to children, and the kind that is possible after you have matured sexually. As long as you are a child, there isn't anything you can do about sex that is going to affect anybody else's life very much.

When parents understand that this is a part of normal development and treat it just as they do any other form of behavior in which a child needs guidance in social rules, the youngster soon passes on to a more mature stage, and nobody is harmed in the least. But sex expression on an adult basis, which is sexual intercourse, with impregnation of a girl as a possible result, may have a very marked effect upon other people's lives.

I have dwelt at length upon the fact that mankind differs

from other animals in being capable of love, and in a need for it. There is one other very important way in which we differ from the animals, and that is that human offspring must have love and care for a great many years.

If our children could fend for themselves by the time they were three or six months old, as is the case with most animal children, probably it wouldn't be very important to control sex desires. But I need not tell you that this is not the case. Human offspring have a very thin time of it indeed if they do not have loving parents who will protect them and look after them for twenty-one years or so.

This is one of the major reasons for the institution of marriage—to protect the child until he is grown, and to give him the legal status which assures him the rights due him from his parents. It has been well established—I am sure no one will dispute this point—that it is best for children to be born within a family. The family in modern society has undergone many changes, but a home is still the one source which can offer the utmost comfort, pleasure in sharing family experiences, and the free expression of affection. Children who grow up without the experience of a loving home and parents have a big handicap to overcome.

Even though a boy may offer to marry a girl he has impregnated, such marriages are rather often unhappy, with bitter maladjustment between the parents. They are inclined to blame and to reject each other because of the mistake both made together. Hence, they may fail to provide the child with parents he can respect and admire. When a father and mother did not want their child, it is not always easy for them to conceal this fact. These children at times become mentally ill because they feel that they are alone and unloved and, as a result, are unable to develop the self-esteem and confidence necessary for a successful life. Such children can really sense whether or not they are loved by their parents. They can quickly tell by their parents' actions and attitudes when the parents have real affection and love for them.

Suppose the couple do not marry. As you probably know, society looks with disfavor upon children who are born out of wedlock. I grant this is not fair, and wish it were otherwise, but it has been society's way of impressing the need for parents to be responsible, and to bring up their children under conditions which are satisfactory for both the parents and the child.

Any man who follows his primitive urges about sex expression, without regard to society's rules, runs the risk of dooming the offspring that may result to difficult and unhappy lives. Innocent, helpless babies may have to pay the price for his sexual indulgence. That is the reason why men of any age should control their sexual desires. No manly man would ask another adult to take the consequences of his own wrongdoing. How much less would a manly man, if he were to stop and think about it, ask a baby, a child, an adolescent, to foot a bill of unhappiness and suffering for his father's uncontrolled impulses?

The illegitimate child is in no way responsible for his situation. The man who brought him into being is the one who deserves the bad names that are too often applied to those born out of wedlock. If we were logical about this thing, there would be no shame in being illegitimate, but there would be deep shame for the man who was responsible for a child's being born into the world without a home and without a proper place in society.

The primitive urges which offend others or bring hurt to them are the ones that must be controlled if people are to live together and have a good society. There is no primitive impulse that can work more lasting harm on others, if uncontrolled, than the sex urge. Even though a man may escape the more obvious consequences himself for his indulgence, if he is mature and intelligent he will not foist them off on someone else.

So far as full sex expression during the teen years is concerned, here is a point on which Nature herself is somewhat contradictory. It is true that around the age of fourteen, as I have pointed out, the average boy begins having erections, his body begins to manufacture spermatozoa, and he has strong impulses to put his new sex powers into effect. In very simple societies, as I mentioned before, where making a living is a question of being good at hunting or fishing, marriages often take place at any time after a boy has matured physically and a girl has menstruated.

However, there are indications that Nature does not intend for people to produce offspring before they are in their early twenties. The body and the sexual organs continue to grow and to mature for years after the first emissions of semen, or the first menstruation. The death rate of both mothers and babies is higher in the teens, and mothers who have not fully matured are more prone to miscarriage—that is, have a baby die in the womb or be born before it is developed enough so it can live outside the mother. The same thing is true in the animal world.

Aristotle, the old Greek philosopher, observed that in cities where marriage at an early age was the rule, the people were small and weak. He added that women who marry too early are inclined to be wanton, and that the bodily frame in men will be stunted if they marry "while the seed is growing."

However that may be, in our society a teen-ager has a number of special reasons for controlling his sexual impulses until he is in a position to give them full scope without harm to himself or to anyone else. First of all, as a rule he is not in a position economically to support a family. To tie himself down with obligations of this kind so early in life is to lose his youth and the freedom from adult responsibility which is one of the advantages of being young.

Second, to have full sexual expression now may defeat his own best interests. It is very likely to interfere with his preparation for life, in the way of schooling, or of attaining skills that will fit him for a good position. Moreover, it is always well to remember that the girl who appeals to you in the teen-years may not have the same appeal when you are older. You may find yourself tied to a mate whom you wouldn't have chosen at all once you are in the twenties. This doesn't always happen, of course. Sometimes an immature couple can grow up together and have a very happy life. But too often in such cases, one will mature and develop adult attitudes and interests while the other may develop much more slowly and the interests may be in entirely different directions.

I don't think that society is too unreasonable in asking teen-agers to wait for adulthood before having adult sex expression. In return for the control you exercise in this respect, you are given advantages which few generations before you have enjoyed. First, and terribly important to your future happiness, you have the opportunity to find a vocation you will enjoy and to prepare yourself for it.

Second, you are offered the boon of light-hearted good times, without danger of incurring adult burdens and responsibilities prematurely. (I don't want to make these seem too gruesome. The fact is that we welcome them and enjoy them when we are ready for them. It is when we are not ready that they are hard and grueling.)

Third, as I said in the last chapter, you have the privilege of getting to know a number of girls, so that you can have a much better idea of what you will want in a wife.

Sexual indulgence too early in the game can defeat one or all of these purposes and advantages of the teen years. This is in addition to moral considerations, which should by no means be disregarded. The moral laws represent the wisdom society has gained through the experience of many generations. If you examine them, you find that their purpose is to keep men and women from actions that will harm them, and harm society too. I am perhaps more aware of these factors than many people are, because I have had to deal so many times with the difficulties that people get themselves and others into when they break the moral laws. That is one reason why I hope strongly that teen-agers who read this book will derive all the joys and benefits of wholesome companionship with girls, which we discussed in the chapter before this, without endangering their own goals for the future, and without creating problems for the society of which they are a part.

9. Perils of Incontinence

In the "good old days," when our grandparents and parents were young, a young man's education was not considered complete until he was given, in strict privacy and by some supposedly wise older person, a "man to man" lecture on the perils of sex. This talk was usually vague, and the dangers were usually unspecified. The idea was to scare the young man into continent behavior. I doubt that this idea of continence through fear was ever very effective, and in some cases, as we have seen, it was harmful.

We know, now, that the enjoyment of a good life comes with an education that gives knowledge and understanding, and develops healthy reasoning powers. In this chapter, then, I shall relate some of the experiences with which I have dealt as a doctor and health commissioner, not to "scare" but to encourage the knowledge and understanding that will give you good reasons for refraining from unwise sex behavior.

Most of us learn quite early in life that there are criminal aspects of sex. Our newspapers and other periodicals, movies, stories, and sometimes just hearsay, hint about or describe in detail criminal sexual practices. The accounts, however, are often written from a news or story viewpoint so that the facts of the sex crime are not clear. For instance, from time to time, we read of a doctor or other person who has been brought to court as an abortionist, but the young person may have no conception of the tragic sequence of events that led to this person's arrest as a criminal.

When a shamed and terrified teen-age girl walks into her family doctor's office and tearfully tells him she is pregnant though unmarried, she may not realize that he cannot legally terminate her pregnancy and thereby help her to save face with her family and friends. He may know the girl well and be greatly moved by her unhappy situation. But a reputable professional man must refuse to help in this particular way.

Doctors take a very solemn vow to save life, wherever it is possible to do so. It is not our business to kill. Under medical ethics and under the law as well, a doctor may not interrupt a pregnancy except in the case of what is called a "therapeutic abortion"—that is, when he believes that the mother will die if the pregnancy is not brought to an end. Even then doctors proceed with the utmost caution, and always get another medical opinion before they take this drastic step. A therapeutic abortion, deemed necessary to save a mother's life, is carried out in a hospital, with everything at hand to stop a hemorrhage, or to prevent infection.

For this is the second consideration the doctor must take into account. To dislodge a strong, healthy embryo or fetus from the mother's womb is a risky business. Death is very much more likely to result from an operation of this kind than from childbirth. Where it is simply a case of an unwanted baby, not only would the unborn child be destroyed, but the doctor knows that the mother might lose her life as well. This is a kind of double murder, which no reputable doctor will take any chance of committing.

Then there is the legal aspect. If it is found out that a

doctor has yielded to this particular plea, he will face a term in the penitentiary and will be barred forevermore from the practice of medicine. It takes a great many years of study and struggle to produce a doctor—there is no other profession which calls for as long and as intensive training. Anyone who asks a doctor to perform an illegal operation is in effect asking him to throw all this overboard, commit a crime and possibly wreck his whole future, to save a couple from the consequences of an act for which the doctor himself was in no way responsible.

I have gone into this at some length, because young people are entitled to know that the consequences of a sex act cannot be banished by some safe, magical process. Once a baby is started into the world, there is no going back to things the way they were before. This is one mistake you can't undo just by being sorry you made it.

The great majority of men and women who perform criminal abortions (operations to get rid of an unwanted baby) are without medical training, and unfitted to deal with the complications that may easily arise. As Health Commissioner of Chicago, it is part of my job to hunt out and deal with people like this, who often bring death or suffering upon the girls and women who resort to them. Some of the situations we encounter would make your blood run cold. A few abortionists maintain some standards of cleanliness and antisepsis, but a girl in terrible trouble cannot be particular, and the majority of those who profess to "help her" pay little heed to these factors. All they are interested in is, first, to get their money, and second, that if a girl is going to die, she won't die on their premises. A girl who goes to an abortionist literally takes her life in her hands.

And for those who survive, often the end result is sterility. The Fallopian tubes may be sealed by an infection resulting from the abortion so that the ova cannot pass on to the uterus. In later life, when the girl is married and longing for a child, it is impossible for her to become a mother. Rarely does the husband in such a case know the true reason for his wife's inability to become pregnant, and why he must miss parenthood too.

Quite often, after an abortion, hospitalization becomes necessary if the girl's life is to be saved. Any physician who is aware that an abortion has been performed must, upon admitting the patient to the hospital, report such a matter to the District Attorney's office. The girl, the boy responsible for the pregnancy, and both sets of parents are questioned in order to press charges, if possible, against the person committing the abortion. This is a shaming and painful experience for all involved and especially for the young girl who is already physically ill and emotionally disturbed. A court case may later follow at which time the story may break in the newspapers. Then the entire community is aware of the situation. Often this is the end of a girl's life which should just be beginning, and families have to move to new communities to start all over again.

Even though none of the foregoing results come about, the experience of abortion is degrading to a young girl and a serious physical and emotional shock. All the rest of her life she may blame herself for having done a great wrong, refrain from marriage, and forfeit all chances for a happy family life. Or, overcome by remorse, she may develop a serious mental disorder in the form of depression, and make a suicidal attempt. In my long experience, I have seen more cases of these unpleasant kinds than I like to remember.

In other cases, the girl may protest that she loves the father of her baby, and wants to marry him and have the child. The boy, too, may be willing for this, but he may be under the age at which he can marry without his parents' consent, and his parents may have refused their permission for the marriage. Often they blame the girl, consider her a bad girl, and accuse her of having tried deliberately to lure their son into marriage. Or the boy may deny his responsibility or try to implicate other boys, and paternity, necessitating blood tests, may be difficult to prove. If the girl files charges against the father of her illegitimate child and demands support for it, this too involves publicity which neither she nor her family may wish to endure.

Many unmarried girls do not seek or find a way out of the dilemma and in due time give birth to an illegitimate child. At times this is accomplished alone, without benefit of medical or hospital care. Under these circumstances it may be a temptation to destroy the child, and all of us have read lurid newspaper accounts of murder of their children by frightened, desperate girls who take this chance.

Helpful parents, or the girl herself, may arrange to have the baby born in a hospital. Then there arises the problem of the disposal of the infant. It may be that the family wants no one to know about it, and the girl is willing to give the baby away. Although she loves the child and wants to keep it, she may be persuaded that without a father it will be ostracized and rejected by society. Giving it in adoption may be the solution, for there are many married couples who are childless and eager to adopt children as their own.

However, every state has laws regarding the adoption of children. In a number of states it is required that investiga-

tors of approved child welfare agencies give testimony
relating to children to be given in adoption, and to the
children's parents as well. Unless they have the co-operation of the mother of an illegitimate child, it is impossible
for them to obtain mental and physical examinations of
the child, and information about the parents. Many girls
are unwilling to give reputable social agencies this information, fearing to reveal any facts about themselves or the
identity of the father of the child. In this connection "black
market" activities you have probably read about come into
play, which enable a girl to give up her baby shortly after
its birth. She signs the necessary papers and the child is
taken away by the new parents, who although they may
have sufficient money to pay an exorbitant fee for the transaction, may be entirely unsuited to assume the role of parents, and the child may lead a miserably unhappy life.

These are pretty grim and serious matters we have been
talking about. They are so ugly and sordid that we older
people have a natural tendency to shield young folks from
knowledge of them. But they have happened to many teen-
agers as a result of sexual incontinence. And when these
things can happen and do happen all around us, I believe
it is your right to know about them.

I wouldn't want you to think that the family doctor can
do nothing to save a girl and a baby from one of the sordid
and awful fates I have just described. If a girl permits him
to do so, he can help her by breaking the sad news to her
parents, and with them decide how best to handle the situation, from the standpoint of the girl's future and the
baby's welfare. If the parents are harsh and rejecting, as
sometimes happens, then the doctor can put the girl in
touch with an agency or institution which will care for her,

and protect the baby's interests. This is far too big and serious a situation for the average teen-ager to handle alone, and I would beg and implore young folks who do get into this kind of trouble to make a clean breast to their parents or their family doctor or both. But, of course, I would urge most of all that young folk should refrain from the kind of act that may land them in this kind of trouble.

It is a further part of your education in sex to know that the penalties of incontinence are not always borne entirely by the girl. I have known many cases where a teen-age boy has had to pay heavily. I did not wonder that Mrs. Jones was on the verge of a nervous breakdown when she told me what was troubling her. Her son Jack was one of the most promising boys I have ever seen. He was the star athlete of his high school. He got good grades with practically no effort, he was known as the most popular boy in school. On the basis of his personality and achievements, he had won a scholarship to an excellent college. Naturally he was the apple of his parents' eyes, and they confidently expected him to have a brilliant career.

It was sex that proved Jack's downfall. "The girls have been after him since he was twelve," his mother told me. "Even their parents would invite him to late dinners at the country club, when he was just a child. Girls called him up, they threw themselves at him in every conceivable way."

That would not have been a sad fate in itself, as I am sure you will agree, but a particular girl succeeded in engaging Jack's attention. She flattered him, built up his already rather inflated ego, made it her business in life to have Jack enjoy her company. Jack's parents viewed the situation with some concern, because she was one of those girls whose parents pay no heed to what is going on. She could stay out until any hour of the night. Her parents were seldom at home, and she and Jack could have the house to themselves almost any evening that they chose. The Joneses worried, and with reason, and breathed a sigh of relief when the girl graduated a year ahead of Jack, and their son showed signs of losing interest in her.

But this girl did not give up so easily. She came to the school every day and had lunch with Jack in the cafeteria. She would wait for him at the school, or practice field, in her car. Jack couldn't get rid of her without being brutal about it, and a situation of this kind is a good deal for a teen-age boy to manage. The Joneses got the coach to talk to the girl, and then the school principal, to no effect.

Finally the thing the Joneses had been dreading came about. Sexual relations were entered upon, and the girl became pregnant. She admitted frankly that she had done what she could to bind Jack to her. It was easy to understand that Jack himself had seen no very good reason for refusing what was offered him so freely. And so the elder Joneses had to stand by and see this promising life head for shipwreck.

When they learned that the inevitable had happened, the girl's parents suddenly became very conscious of their daughter's moral welfare. They threatened legal prosecution unless Jack married her. Jack's parents sorrowfully conceded that he should face the consequences of his act, and in any event they did not want their grandchild to be branded as illegitimate. Jack dropped out of high school a few months before he was to have graduated, gave up all thought of college, married the girl and got a job.

"Dr. Bundesen, I can hardly bear it!" Mrs. Jones sobbed

—and I could not blame her for feeling as she did. "Jack never really cared for her, it was just that she made everything so easy for him. I went to see them yesterday. Here they are living in one room, a baby on the way, and they haven't the faintest idea what it is all about. They don't know what to do with a baby, they don't know what to do with themselves! Why did this have to happen to Jack?"

Many a young fellow has had to marry long before he was ready for this step, give up his education, alter his whole life, because of sexual incontinence. Perhaps he does not even care whole-heartedly for the girl or think she is the type of girl he would otherwise choose to marry. Perhaps he has reason to believe she is promiscuous, and has no certainty that the child is his.

Where a boy belongs to a well-to-do family, the "easy" girl or her parents have been known to use sex relations as a basis for blackmail. Sexual incontinence can lay one open to a world of sordidness and greed.

Even when the teen-ager who impregnates a girl believes that he loves her and wants to marry her, it may be long before he is economically independent and able to support a family, or emotionally mature enough to assume the responsibilities of family life and the education of children. Probably he has not completed his education, and giving up his studies at an early age will change his whole future. If the couple finally decide to marry, the union is almost certain to be unhappy, with bitter maladjustment between them, because each feels that the other was responsible for the loss of carefree youth and dreams.

No fine boy wants to inflict upon a young girl he admires and respects the injustice of urging upon her an illicit love which subjects her to the dangers and consequences of an illegitimate pregnancy. A manly man puts women and children first in matters of life and death. He recognizes the importance and beauty of the woman's role in the bearing of children. He knows that a thinking man is expected to see to it that future mothers are not debased to the point where the children to whom they give life, will always be a symbol to them of guilt and shame. No boy likes to see this happen to a girl in his family; every father is embittered and outraged when it happens to his daughter.

Right here I can hear somebody asking, "But what about prostitutes? Such considerations do not apply to them. With them sex is a business transaction, and there are none of the penalties you have mentioned. Why need a man feel any compunctions about availing himself of their services when sex urges become troubling?"

I know that this point comes up among college men, and even among highschoolers. There is always somebody—and often this is an older man—ready to argue that it is a part of the growing up of a male to visit a house of prostitution, or to gain sex experience with a prostitute. I have known a group of young fellows to take a sudden notion to enlarge their knowledge of life in this way, and to hunt up a brothel as a kind of adventure. One who declines to participate is branded a sissy. Prostitutes often accost young men on city streets, and offer their bodies in the most persuasive ways at their command. Sometimes this is a temptation that is hard to resist, unless one knows about the dangers and degradation that accompany prostitution.

This happens to be one more unpleasant phase of life with which I have to deal in my official capacity, since the control of venereal disease is an aspect of my job as health officer. I have seen a great many prostitutes in my time, and know better than most people what a horrible blot this institution is upon any society that calls itself civilized.

The basis of prostitution is the so-called special need of men to express their lower natures. Since in any kind of civilization it is recognized that "decent" women should not be used for mere animal pleasure, unaccompanied by love, incontinent men turn to women who do not seem to care what society thinks of them. This is not always the case though. A certain number of young girls slip into prostitution through lack of training for respectable jobs, and because they have had a raw deal either from their homes or from some man, or from both. A certain number are inveigled into it by false representations. The "White Slave" traffic about which we used to hear so much is still prevalent, and pretty girls have to be on guard in answering certain types of glamorous advertisements for positions. Once a girl has been tricked into commercialized vice, it may be very difficult for her to extricate herself.

The "working life" of a prostitute is of short duration, for such attractiveness to males as a girl may possess doesn't last long in the conditions to which she is subjected. Since they associate intimately with every type of man, prostitutes are prime victims for violent ends. In some cities, the police hardly bother to investigate the murder of a prostitute, it is such a routine matter, and so much to be expected. If a prostitute isn't murdered, or doesn't die young from disease or drink or drugs—further occupational hazards of prostitution—or stick her head in a gas oven or purposely take an overdose of sleeping pills, as many prostitutes do, her later life is likely to be dragged out in abject poverty.

Since prostitution panders to the unbridled animal natures of men, it is also allied with all the basest features of our society. A great many men live off the earnings of prostitutes, and exploit these women as though they were draft animals. Many brothels are owned by gangsters and other criminals, who will not hesitate to rob, or even kill, unwary patrons. Indeed, many prostitutes lure men to dives where they will be "rolled"—that is, given knockout drops or assaulted, and robbed. This is a danger for young service men, especially. Prostitutes are the great spreaders of venereal disease, a subject we shall go into more fully in the next chapter.

We men can hardly be proud of the fact that billions of dollars go every year to commercialized vice. The sexual incontinence of otherwise "good" citizens provides luxury and power for our most despicable and vicious criminals. It bribes officials and gives gangsters control of many phases of government. It provokes murders, and helps to cover them up. The money spent this way would be ample to prepare the female victims of commercialized vice for useful work, and to care for those who are unfit to work. The worst blight and cesspool of our society would then be wiped out.

I don't want you to think that I abhor prostitutes. As a matter of fact, no group in our society is more tragic. These women are human beings, and they would be as fine and decent as anyone if they had met with fineness and decency. To say that they are human sacrifices to male lust may sound melodramatic, but it is no more than the truth. I do abhor the existence of prostitution. No man who respects himself or humanity would have any part of this awful thing. A mature thoughtful man pities a prostitute with all his heart, but he would embrace a leper as soon as he would have sexual intercourse with her.

To refrain from acts which may affect one's own life adversely or wreck another's is not being a sissy. It is being smart, in the first place, and a considerate, thoughtful person in the second place. Don't let anyone tell you differently!

10. Venereal Disease

Just as the most dramatic danger for a girl in illicit sex relations is the chance that she may become pregnant, the most dramatic danger for a man is that he may contract one of the so-called "social" or venereal diseases. When our ancestors gave those portentous, man-to-man talks, that was probably what was chiefly in their minds.

However, until quite recently, venereal disease in any of its forms was considered more or less like a dirty word. So-called refined people did not speak of it, and usually about the only information young folks received was that some dreadful thing might happen to them if they broke the moral laws. Warnings of this kind, which give you no real idea of what to look out for and why you should look out for it, are not too effective. Under this policy of silence, syphilis and other venereal diseases flourished.

As I write this, the battle to bring venereal disease out into the open so that it can be simply dealt with, is recent history. The public health officers and others who waged this battle had to face a great wall of resistance, but finally success resulted. Today these words can be spoken without causing anyone to recoil or faint. The problems posed by venereal disease can be discussed, and that is the opening wedge to doing away with them. Venereal disease is far from licked, but the program of education we have had in the past fifteen years or so is at least making it possible for young men to know what it is and how it comes about, and is making treatment available where the disease exists. It will require eternal vigilance to completely conquer venereal diseases. However, education of the public in venereal disease is enabling us to save a great many innocent babies —thousands of them—from paying a heavy price for the sex sins of a father or mother. I feel that the more people know about the social diseases, the sooner the day will come when we can wipe them out entirely.

Just how long men and women have had venereal diseases is not absolutely known. Some people believe that illnesses described by ancient writers were venereal disease, and that some of the laws of cleanliness and moral behavior laid down by Moses were intended to combat it. They feel that it may have existed in Europe in mild form from the beginning of the Christian era, if not long before, but these are questions that probably cannot be settled now.

To all intents and purposes, syphilis, considered the worst of the venereal diseases, first became known and descended upon Europe in the year 1494, just two years after Columbus discovered America, and he and his sailors had spent some time in the West Indies.

Ever since that time, syphilis has wrought havoc in the civilized world. It has altered the course of history. Henry VIII of England, who was born in 1491 and died in 1547, was the most illustrious known sufferer from it. A handsome, brilliant, golden-haired lad when he assumed the throne at the age of eighteen, adored by his people, he had perhaps the sunniest prospects of any monarch ever born. Medical historians believe that he acquired syphilis in early adolescence, and that is probably why his first Queen Catherine was never able to bear a living male child. It is known that she had several miscarriages and stillbirths, a typical result when a wife has acquired syphilis from her husband. "Bloody" Queen Mary, the one child Catherine was able to bring into the world alive, had the structural signs of a person born with congenital syphilis, that is, acquired from the mother before birth or at the time of birth. Anne Boleyn, also, for whom Henry defied the Pope and broke away from the Catholic Church, had the tragedy of miscarrying several times after her daughter Elizabeth was born. The great, handsome, likeable king grew increasingly morose, cruel and unpredictable. In spite of his succession of six wives, three of whom he had beheaded, only one live son was born to him, and that a sickly boy who died young. Henry himself died with some symptoms like those of late syphilis, such as large ulcers on both legs, and paralysis. Medical authorities believe that if Henry's wives could have been examined by present methods, all would have been found syphilitic except Anne of Cleves, who managed cleverly to foil Henry in his attempts to consummate their marriage.

There are five kinds of venereal disease, so called because they are associated with venery, or sexual promiscuity, the word venery in its turn coming from Venus, the goddess of love. They are acquired, except for a tiny handful of cases, in the same way—by sexual intercourse with a person infected by the disease. About the only exceptions to this rule are the germs transmitted by kissing when there is a venereal sore on the lips or in the mouth. Also, doctors and laboratory people who come in contact with the germs in treatment or in laboratory research may become infected.

Thus it is possible to get a venereal disease in other ways than intercourse, but it happens rarely.

Many a wife has contracted a venereal disease from her husband, as a result of promiscuous relationships he has had before or during marriage. Occasionally a husband contracts it from a wife who has had promiscuous relationships before or during marriage. But if both have refrained from promiscuous relationships and continue to do so, there is practically no danger that they will acquire a venereal disease from a public toilet or other inanimate object.

The various venereal diseases are caused by different types of organisms, as we shall see presently, but all these organisms have one trait in common—outside the human body they are frail and die quickly. The medium favorable to them is a warm, moist mucous membrane, such as is found in the genital tracts of the male and female and in the lips and mouth. Thus, we physicians know that close contact with a person infected is almost a necessity, and that in the great majority of cases it comes through contact of the genital organs. That is why those who control sex and limit it to a marital partner have little if anything to fear from V.D.

The venereal diseases have certain similarities, but each reacts upon the human body in a different way, and in the main different types of treatment are required. Since syphilis is the most serious and deadly of the venereal diseases, we will consider it first.

Syphilis

Syphilis has a number of names besides its official one. It is occasionally referred to as the "pox," and may also be called "lues," "bad blood" and "hard chancre." Physicians speak of it as the "Great Imitator," because its symptoms may be confused with those of a number of other diseases, and also the "Killer," because so many people die of it each year. It is caused by a germ called a spirochete, which is slender and shaped like a corkscrew, and can be seen only under a powerful microscope. Delicate and easily killed outside the body, spirochetes are very strong and stubborn once they are entrenched in the system, multiply rapidly and may attack any one part of the body or many parts.

The first symptom, a sore called a chancre (pronounced "shanker") appears at the point where the germ entered the body—on the penis, generally, in the case of a male—and usually about three weeks after exposure. However, the chancre may appear in ten days, or not until three months have passed. The chancre is not painful and may not be noticed at all. This is more likely to happen with women, when the sore is hidden inside the vulva or the vagina or on the neck of the uterus. This is called the primary stage, and since the chancre swarms with rapidly multiplying spirochetes, the syphilis sufferer at this point is highly dangerous to anyone with whom he or she may have sexual relations. Even without treatment, however, the chancre will disappear in anywhere from a few days to a few weeks.

The second group of symptoms, called the secondary stage, appears anywhere from four to eight weeks after the chancre has vanished. Uusually there is a skin eruption. This may be severe or mild, and may cover the whole body or only a small area of it. The victims may also have headache, fever, sore throat, pain in the bones and joints, swollen lymph glands, and sores in the mouth. These last are highly infectious. In many cases, some hair falls out. The symptoms vary in severity with different people. Some may be aware of only a little discomfort, some may be practically disabled. But the secondary stage disappears, too, after a time, whether it is treated or not. Syphilis is most infectious during the primary and secondary stages and one prostitute has been known to infect innumerable men. But this is also the time when it yields most easily to treatment, and a cure is most likely to be effected. The treatment that cures the syphilis, if followed consistently, will also render the sufferer non-infectious.

However, if nothing is done, the disease enters the third, or latent stage. The outward signs disappear, but the germs attack the vital inner structures of the body. In some few persons the germs always remain latent, but in most sufferers damage goes on undercover, which shows itself finally in what is called "late syphilis." Then it may be found that the blood vessels and heart have been injured, causing heart disease and death; or the brain damaged, causing the kind of insanity that is called paresis. Or, syphilis may attack the spinal cord, causing a peculiar, stumbling kind of walk that is labeled locomotor ataxia. If it has invaded the eyes or ears, the result may be blindness or deafness. Or, areas of body tissue may be eaten away by tumor-like growths.

One of its most ghastly features is that a syphilitic mother who is not treated may pass on the disease to her unborn child, if, that is, the child is born alive. The rate of miscarriage and stillbirth—when a baby is born dead—is very high among syphilitic mothers, and many syphilitic babies who are alive at birth die in early infancy. If they survive, they may show symptoms of syphilis in their first few months, and become victims of late syphilis in their teens or twenties.

This happens if the mother is not treated. But one encouraging thing is that now doctors do have treatments that are most effective if they are applied in the primary or secondary stages of the disease and are also effective in all stages of syphilis. In Chicago we have clinics where pregnant women who have syphilis are treated free of charge. We, just as doctors everywhere, have the gratification of seeing the great majority of these babies born healthy and free of syphilis. Thanks to penicillin, what used to be a long-drawn-out and frequently ineffective course of medication now is given in a short time, and is generally quite effective unless too much damage has been done to the vital organs.

You have probably heard of the Wassermann test, in which a sample of blood is taken and subjected to various procedures which aid in determining whether or not syphilis is present. Slightly different types of tests, the Kahn and other precipitation tests, are used for the same purpose. To protect innocent adults and unborn children, many states today require evidence that an applicant for a marriage license is not infected with syphilis, or, if infected, shall be treated sufficiently to prevent progress or spread of the disease before being allowed to marry.

Gonorrhea

This disease has even more nicknames than syphilis, and is referred to as "clap," "dose," "strain," "gleet," "the drip" and "running." It is not considered as serious as syphilis because it rarely kills people, but physicians call it the

"Crippler" because it can disable. It can also cause blindness, and it has rendered many men and women sterile, that is, incapable of producing children.

The germ that causes gonorrhea is called gonococcus, and is shaped much like a coffee bean. The first symptoms usually appear from three to five days after exposure, but they may show up in a day or so, or not for two weeks. A male victim usually has a feeling of itching and irritation in the urethra, which runs through the penis. When he passes urine there may be a burning sensation, and a few hours later there may be a discharge of yellow pus. Unless treatment is started, the germs are likely to work their way back from the end of the penis, where they entered the urethra, and may spread to the prostate gland, or affect the testicles, causing them to swell and be painful. Untreated gonorrhea quite frequently blocks the tubes through which the sperm cells pass. If both tubes are blocked in this way, the man may never be able to have children. In the same way, when infection spreads through the reproductive organs of a woman and blocks the Fallopian tubes, she may never be able to become pregnant.

If a woman with gonorrhea does bear a child, the germs may get into the baby's eyes as it passes through the birth canal, causing inflammation or blindness. That is why many states have laws requiring that drops of silver nitrate be placed in the eyes of every newborn baby.

Germs of gonorrhea, introduced into the eyes of adults, multiply rapidly and can do more damage even than to babies. Gonorrhea also may cause arthritis—that is why it is called the "Crippler." In a few rare cases, the germs lodge in the heart, multiply there, and cause death.

Where gonorrhea is suspected, a sample of the pus from

the genital organs may be studied under a microscope to see if gonococci are present, or the organism may be grown and identified. The sulfa drugs have been fairly effective in the treatment of gonorrhea, but during the last decade, penicillin has been found more so. Treatment may bring relief from symptoms and render the sufferer non-infectious to others, but if the tubes which convey the male sperm or the female ova have been blocked, there is little to be done about the resulting sterility.

Syphilis and gonorrhea are the two venereal diseases most prevalent among white people. There are three more which are found largely in tropical countries, and in various portions of the South in our own country. However, these diseases may appear anywhere and anyone who is sexually reckless may incur them. I shall therefore describe them briefly:

Chancroid

The germ of chancroid is called the "Ducrey bacillus," and is slender and short with rounded ends. The disease starts with a chancre or sore on the penis of the male or the vulva of the female, as the case may be. Sometimes it causes a large swelling in the groin, which breaks open and drains, like a boil. If the condition is not treated, great ulcers may appear on the genital organs, and eventually destroy portions of them. The sulfa drugs, either taken by mouth or sprinkled in powder form on the sores, usually effect a cure.

Granuloma Inguinale

A round or oval bacillus called the "Donovan body" causes this disease. It first may appear on the genitals or

buttocks or around the anus as little swellings or protuber-
ances. The skin surface breaks, leaving an ulcer with a
beefy-red color which bleeds easily if it is pressed. The
ulcers may persist for years if they are not treated. The
disease may also cause an increase in the size of the penis
or scrotum, and possibly bring about destruction of the
genital organs. It may spread to other exterior parts of the
body.

Lymphopathia Venereum

This fifth of the venereal diseases is caused by a filterable
virus, instead of a germ. The first symptom is a sore that
appears on the penis or scrotum. It looks a good deal like
a big pimple or blister, is painless, and disappears in due
time. The second phase is a spreading through the lymph
nodes which are just under the skin in the region of the
groin. The groin may swell up into what are called
"buboes," sores filled with pus. Sometimes a running ulcer
results. The penis or scrotum may become three times
normal size, and the victim may have headache, fever, chills,
abdominal aches, pains in the joints, and loss of appetite.

The treatment of this disease has not been too satisfactory, especially if it has been of long duration. The best
bets to date are the sulfa drugs and some of the new anti-
biotics.

There is one thing to remember about all these diseases.
Exposure occurs through a change of sexual partners, and
the extent of the spread of these diseases in a society depends upon the frequency with which people change sexual
partners. One may acquire a social disease from just one
partner, but it is much more likely to happen if one changes

partners often. The man who has sexual relations only with his wife, a fine girl who has had no relations with any man but him, runs no risk of contracting a venereal disease. But the more persons a man has sexual relations with, the greater his chances for acquiring disease, and the more quickly it spreads throughout a community. The more promiscuous and profligate a society becomes, the higher its rate of V.D.

There has been one rather unexpected result of the educational program we have carried on about V.D. in recent years. As I mentioned in the last chapter, prostitutes were previously the great spreaders and that has been true since 1494. Recently, however, men have been alerted to the danger of prostitutes and, moreover, health authorities and progressive doctors everywhere have encouraged vigorous campaigns to eliminate organized prostitution, and treat and rehabilitate such infected women.

Now an increasing number of cases arise from promiscuous relationships among friends, or with non-professional pick-ups in taverns, bars, restaurants, dance halls and the streets. As long as a girl is not a professional prostitute, a man may have the idea that it is safe to have sexual relations with her, but today the girl who can be "talked" into sexual relations may be as great a danger in this way as a streetwalker. Undoubtedly drinking plays a part in this new kind of promiscuity. People who resort to bars and taverns and are led into sexual incontinence through liquor are among the prime victims for contracting venereal disease.

Or, it arises through the emotionally maladjusted lives to which we have paid considerable attention in this book. One fifteen-year-old girl confessed that she had infected ten classmates with syphilis. Up until a year before, she had led a normal, happy life. Then her mother died, and she was placed in a home where she received little attention and no sexual guidance. Tears came to the girl's eyes as she spoke of her loneliness. But by turning to sex as a way of finding companionship, she had acquired syphilis herself and had passed it on to ten young boys.

In Chicago, we have largely reduced the menace of V.D., so far as its spread by prostitution is concerned, by energetic suppression of these professionals, and free treatment when they are found to be diseased. But we are helpless when it comes to the case of the girl next door, let us say, who may have had only one sexual experience, but that with a boy who had a venereal disease.

Even with the greatly improved methods of treatment, no man who "looks before he leaps" and who respects his own body and his role as a future husband and father, wants to take any chance of incurring one of these diseases. It is a sign of moral weakness to do so, for those who hold to their principles have no need to fear V.D. Also, about the finest heritage you can pass on to your children is a good body and a good brain and good blood. If you have received these things from your ancestors, as I daresay most of you have, one of your great duties to your own offspring and to the race is to transmit them undamaged.

If a young man should betray his ideals and has any reason to believe he has acquired a venereal disease in consequence—as you can see, a sore in the genital area or a burning sensation when urinating or discharge of pus from the penis, following promiscuous sex relations, is a warning signal—of course, the thing to do is to hunt up a reputable physician or venereal disease clinic at once, get a diagnosis and insist upon modern methods of treatment. Stay away from the quacks who advertise in the less reputable mediums, and to whom many men still resort because they are ashamed to confess wrongdoing to their own doctor. The quack is likely to claim that he has cured the disease when the first symptoms disappear—the ones that will disappear anyway, whether they are treated or not. Only if a man goes to a reputable physician or clinic can he be sure that he is really cured, and that the germs are not working in his system, to appear later on in some incurable form. Shame should not stand in the way of cure in such a vital matter.

But it is far better yet to live your life in such a way that you will never have a chance to contract a venereal disease. When men as a group honor and respect virtue in women and cease to urge sexual favors outside of marriage, then these diseases will be done away with.

11. Threats to Continence

Now I am well aware that when young people get into sex messes, it is seldom by deliberate intention. Unless they have been very badly trained and educated, as a rule they want to do the right thing. I think this is as true of boys as it is of girls. The very great majority who have slipped into wrong ways have done so because they hadn't realized the power of the sex urges, and have found themselves in a situation that proved too much for their control.

Nature has worked this thing out very cunningly. Her whole interest—and never forget this—is perpetuation of the species, which is desirable and wonderful when the proper time comes. But until the time does come, we have to be on guard, or else as we have seen before, all our life plans may be upset, or we may bring shame and suffering upon others. How to recognize situations that may become dangerous, and either avoid them altogether, or get out of them before catastrophe occurs, is as much a part of a boy's education in sex as it is of a girl's.

Probably the worst threat to continence that we have today is the institution of petting. As most of you know, this usually means the caressing and the manipulating of the intimate parts of a girl's body, the ones in which exciting pleasures may be aroused.

Recent studies tell us that many college people, for instance, have adopted petting as a way of getting sex release until they are ready to marry. Even younger boys and girls are sometimes told that it is all right to enjoy sex thrills, so long as they stop short of intercourse. I believe that a majority of those who argue for petting as a part of teen-age dating are unaware of the dangers that may lie in this form of indulgence.

As we saw in the chapter on the female reproductive processes, Nature has gone to very great lengths to see that females shall get themselves impregnated. Every month a new egg is made ready, and the womb is built up to receive the embryo which Nature hopes will develop. She has ar-ranged that before and up to the time of ovulation, women shall be their happiest and most outgoing selves, with the strongest appeal for the male. More than that, she has pro-vided the female body with several areas which respond pleasurably to caresses, and arouse sex feelings in the girl or woman who allows herself to be fondled in intimate ways. As we noted previously, the breasts are one such area, and the closer one comes to the genital area, the stronger the sensations that are aroused. Since a woman's whole life is altered and bound around the care of children once she becomes pregnant, we can only surmise that Na-ture has evolved this pleasure mechanism in the female as a way of making her forget the consequences to her of in-tercourse. At any rate it is considered normal and natural for her to desire it, once her emotions have been wrought to a high enough pitch through petting.

Petting has an equally strong effect upon the male. His passions too are aroused by these intimacies, and grow as he feels his partner responding. His male impulse is to complete the act, and he may reach a state where his mind and will can no longer control his animal desires.

That is why, until perhaps twenty years or more ago, strong taboos were erected, not only against intercourse outside of marriage, but against fondling of a girl in forbidden areas of her body by any man except one who was prepared to accept the responsibilities of marriage with her. Human beings had learned from sad experience that liberties of this kind were too likely to lead on to intercourse. Moreover, a woman of intelligence and delicacy has a strong urge to save intimacies associated with intercourse for the man whom she wants to be the father of her children, and to whom she can therefore give herself fully and freely.

After you are married, of course all of this will be a proper prelude to full enjoyment of sex relations. Your wife need feel no shame or hesitation in surrendering herself completely to all the thrills and pleasures Nature intended you both to have, and this is an important part of the mating act.

For the unmarried, however, what petting does is to increase the strength of the sex urges, and make it harder to keep them in check. A great many young couples today find that they do not have the power to control the desires their search for thrills has brought into being. As a result, they pay one or more of the penalties of incontinence which we talked about in the two chapters before this one.

However you may look at it, the institution of petting is unfair to girls, and is likely to harm them, whether they become pregnant or not as a result. Many times the girl who consents to pet does so not because of any physical need of her own, but because she wishes to be attractive and desirable to males—a most normal reaction on the part of an adolescent girl. She has been told that unless she pets, she will get no attentions from boys. Perhaps boys tell her that there is "something wrong with her" unless she consents to pet. A young girl may be ashamed to admit to her parents or other adults that this question has come up in her life, and so she fails to get a mature perspective on the matter.

It must be remembered also that a girl has a special need for tenderness, and is likely to assume that a boy who pets with her loves her, and wants to establish a permanent relationship with her. Boys, on the other hand, because their physiology is different, may pet because of a direct physical need, when they have no serious intentions for the future. They are under the stress of a physical urge which demands release and satisfaction, but the person who supplies it is not particularly important to them. Indeed, I have heard some young men say that they don't pet with girls they respect and care for, but deliberately seek out girls who mean nothing to them, for this purpose. Under these circumstances, a boy who is honest does not want to tell his petting partner that he loves her. When she realizes that he does not, and has merely used her, she loses her self-respect, and her emotions about sex become warped and twisted.

If a boy is willing to deceive her and tell her he loves her, when he does not, in order to obtain sex privileges, she is sure to be hurt and humiliated, and may become bitter about the honesty and dependability of men. Some girls take their revenge on our sex by becoming adept at arousing passions in the male which they have no intention of satisfying. Boys resent this, and call such girls "teasers."

Petting opens up any number of ways in which the sexes can get crossed up with each other, and bitterness and disillusionment enter into relationships which otherwise would be pleasant and happy. Instead of helping to prepare for harmonious marriages later on, they may build attitudes toward the opposite sex which will make the adjustments of marriage more difficult.

No boy or girl can as a rule get into a sex difficulty if intimate parts of the body are kept out of bounds in caresses and love-making. It is true that one can build up to a high pitch of excitement by long, passionate kissing alone. Mature people stop even this when they feel that sex feelings are being too much aroused. A man who loves a girl and has a protective feeling toward her wants to take no chance of leading her into something both will regret. This is a responsibility which the honorable male assumes for himself.

Years ago, all of this was made much easier for both sexes by the fact that girls were chaperoned, and were also taught definitely to deny intimate caresses to any man but a husband. Nowadays young people have much more freedom, and this means that they have to learn to impose controls upon themselves. Few young girls are taught today of the consequences that may result to them from petting. Boys are much more aware of the consequences. You may hear companions describe "hot numbers" by name, and realize that the girl who pets heavily suffers a loss of reputation. When a girl can be persuaded to go the whole way, this too is usually made known to the male population. You wouldn't want this to happen to your sister. If men really believed these things were right, they wouldn't boast of conquests and wouldn't publicize the girls who accord them undue privileges. It can hardly be called manly to perpetuate a practice from which the girls gain nothing, and run the risk of losing everything.

During the years when it is to your own interest to remain continent, the wise course is to keep away from things which stir up desires you are not in a position to gratify. You can have beautiful romance, and embraces which express mutual affection, without this. Rightly constituted girls are grateful to young men who refrain from introducing a sex motif into dating, and like and respect them the more for it. This attitude helps the girls adjust to their feminine role of sweetness and fineness and generosity toward the male, and hence our whole sex gains in the end.

The second major threat to continence as the world is organized today is the intrusion of liquor into teen-age affairs. Liquor as a subject in itself is not the province of this book. I realize that a number who will read it may come from homes where a moderate use of alcohol is part of the family tradition and a social custom in the circle of friends. Where this is the case, late teen-agers are often included in the rite of the cocktail or the glass of sherry before dinner. I am not referring to this. What I am speaking of is the part liquor may play when a couple are out together alone, or in groups where there is no responsible chaperone such as in your own home or in the homes of family friends.

Again I must say that it is only in the last twenty years or so that drinking has played any part worth mentioning in teen-age boy and girl relationships. Before that well-brought-up young girls did not drink, and for a young man to get drunk in the presence of girls was enough to put him outside the social pale.

This, too, was a safeguard. For the effect of alcohol is

to release inhibitions, and when people are at an age when they are having a hard enough struggle anyway to keep sex under control, they don't need this added handicap. I do hope that by this time I am known well enough to have people understand that I don't mean any slap at youth by this, because as a rule boys and girls are clean-cut, whole-some and well-worthwhile youngsters. But young fellows are endowed with powerful sex urges, which it is inadvis-able for them to act upon if they want to make something of their future lives. When you have all your wits about you, there will probably be times when it will require all your grit and determination to resist temptation. So many times nowadays when decent, well-meaning boys and girls get into sex difficulties, we find that it is because their will and judgment had been destroyed by alcohol.

I am thinking of one fine, promising chap that I knew, from an excellent family, who raped the girl he was with and was sent to prison for this serious offense. Nothing in this world could have made him do such a thing if he had been sober. I have known a number who married some companion of a revel on a drunken impulse—girls they wouldn't have been seen on the street with if they had been in their right minds. Many and many have awakened from a drunken stupor to find that they had spent the night with a syphilitic prostitute, for since history began there has been an unholy alliance between alcohol and sex on an animal level. Before effective treatments for venereal dis-ease were found, countless brilliant, promising young lives have been wrecked in this way alone.

Girls are as much affected by alcohol as boys are, and the less experienced a girl is in its use, the more likely she is to react to even a small amount of it. Many innocent girls have found themselves in serious difficulties simply because they did not realize what liquor can do to them. I am thinking of one particularly pitiful case, but not unusual now that it has become an accepted social custom for girls and young women to drink in public places.

The lovely daughter of people I know had arranged to fly to another city to marry her fiancé, a service man who had obtained leave for this purpose before going overseas. They were to meet in a certain hotel and she waited for him in the lobby. Through one of those mischances which so often dog service men, the fiancé's leave was canceled, and the message he sent was not delivered to her. So she waited and waited.

A man in the same service as the fiancé observed her, and offered his assistance. The common service seemed a bond, and they got into conversation. She saw no harm in accepting his invitation to have a drink or so in the cocktail lounge to relieve the tedium of waiting. That is the last thing she remembers. The next morning she woke up in a hotel room, the man had gone, and she did not even know his name! Imagine this girl's feelings when she found that she was pregnant. Imagine her fiancé's feelings, too.

You may have heard some fellow boast that he had "made" a nice girl after he had gotten her tight. He knew well that this could not have happened if the girl's sensibilities and will power had not been dulled by liquor. Many pathetic stories of this kind have been sobbed out to me. The male code of honor stipulates that a man shall take no sex advantage of a girl who doesn't know what she is doing, but it should go farther than this. No teen-age girl should be subjected to the dangers she may incur by being urged to take a drink.

Young people do not need the stimulation of alcohol in order to have a wonderful time together. As with petting, its results are likely to degrade in some way or other. Sometimes a young crowd will consider it "smart" to frequent places where liquor is sold to minors—something that is against the law in most states, and forbidden in decent establishments. Beer joints and bootleg hangouts are not places where teen-agers can have wholesome, happy good times. The girls are subjected to rough talk, to leering appraisals and maybe overtures from a type of older man that they should never have to encounter. It is often in parked cars after sessions of this kind that couples commit acts they later regret bitterly.

Since drinking has become so common, I realize that on occasion it requires a good deal of strength of character to refuse to participate. In my experience with young people, this fact, rather than any particular interest in alcohol, has been responsible for sex tragedies in which liquor has played a part. The victims had felt that to drink was grown-up, and that to decline to drink would brand them as sissy or childish.

Just the opposite is true. Really mature people do the thing they feel is right and sensible, no matter how others may poke fun at them. No decent teen-age girl should be called upon to fend off the violent pawing of a drunken escort, no decent teen-age boy should have to deal with a maudlin date. Nothing is more destructive of the respect each sex should feel for the other. When a girl is under his protection, a manly chap will refrain from "getting liquored up" himself, and will do everything he can to protect the girl from unwise indulgence. He will not take her to places where she may be subjected to rough company and to insult.

You probably know without my telling you how necessary it is to stay away from drugs which destroy inhibitions, among other devastating effects on the human system. But since today highschoolers and even gradeschoolers have been made the objects of the unspeakably vicious drug traffic, I might say here that most young people who have fallen victim have done so because they thought it was "smart" and were looking for a thrill. When young lives are ruined in this way, it is the most pitiful thing I know of. Adults who are truly mature avoid unwholesome thrills as they would a loathsome disease. Those are the ones to emulate, rather than the adults who have messed up their lives in unnecessary ways.

It is not the fault of your generation that petting and drinking have become complications in boy and girl relationship, and please don't think I am scolding or blaming. But your generation does not have to accept a line of conduct that has brought grief to so many, and has so often destroyed the fineness and sweetness of teen-age companionships. Any chap who wants to keep these relationships as they should be—and I am sure that is what young fellows do want—has only to make two resolutions: no petting; no drinking where girls are present unless it is in someone's home, where parents or equally responsible adults are on hand.

I find that many young chaps today have become disgruntled about the state of boy-and-girl relationships. Fine and idealistic themselves, they complain that they can't find girls who share their views. One young man said to me recently, "They get insulted if you DON'T make passes at them." Insofar as this sad statement is true, we must remember it is because the girls have unwisely accepted a code of conduct urged upon them by males for selfish reasons. If you were to talk to these girls frankly, you would find that this is not what they want at all. They have simply been paying a price they thought they had to pay to get attention and tenderness from the male.

Boys can reverse this trend any time they wish by giving attention and consideration to girls without exacting sex privileges in return. The girls will love you for it, and I believe that you will find more pleasure and profit in heterosexual relationships without a constant battle to control sex, than with it.

12. Things You May Encounter

In the previous chapter we took a look at practices which have been permitted in many instances to enter into teen-age dating, and which make it harder for boys and girls who adopt them to maintain their own ideals. These are things over which a boy and girl themselves have control. By deliberately choosing to omit petting and liquor or at least to hold them in bounds, they can avoid the greatest threats to their ideals and to their future goals alike.

However, as a boy goes along in the teen years, he is likely to be subjected to situations which are not of his own making, and for which his previous experience has not prepared him. It is your right to know how to evaluate such situations, and how to deal with them, if they should happen to cross your path.

As I have said before, a boy approaching manhood is entitled to learn about the power of sex and the relationships between men and women. This is just as legitimate a field for study and thought as any other. But there is a big difference between the sources from which information of this kind may be obtained.

Few teen-age boys and girls, too, escape an introduction at some time or other to erotic literature and erotic pictures, of a kind forbidden by the law, and hence for sale in under-cover ways. Such literature presents the animal phases of human intercourse. It is seldom concerned with the effect upon us, as human beings, of degrading practices. Hence it is unrealistic, however much it may pretend to be unveiling sexual practices in a realistic way.

That is the difference between under-the-counter erotic literature and the great literary classics which deal with sex realistically, exploring the effect upon character and personality of the men and women who break society's rules, and uncovering the experiences and emotions which have led them into the course of action they have adopted.

The under-the-counter erotica have only one purpose—to inflame sex desire, of which adolescents and all other human beings in the sexually active years have an ample amount anyway. In addition, they give a warped and distorted view of sex, which degrades men and women to the animal level. Books of this kind make it harder, rather than easier, to think of girls in the right way and to realize the force for good that sex should play in one's life.

There can be no profit in letting poison of this kind enter your mind. It can only be disturbing, upsetting and degrading. You learn nothing from it, for it is not a true picture. Most libraries contain many novels and scientific books which do give true pictures of the many aspects of sex in the lives of human beings. Explore these as you like, but don't soil your thoughts and ideals with the kind of thing that is written to serve this purpose alone.

Then there is a kind of literature, not out-and-out pornographic and often found in so-called "smart" magazines and in best-selling novels, which stresses freedom in sex and makes it seem an accepted thing. This concept has even crept into detective stories—in one type, the good-looking, virile, private "eye" is always being besieged by lovely

ladies who embrace him passionately at their first meeting,
and express a willingness to go to bed with him. It is not
fashionable at present to picture any unpleasant consequences as flowing from these free and unabashed matings.
Many young girls get their mistaken notions about the way
women should behave from stories which glamorize sexual
looseness, and do not give the other side of the picture, the
one a girl finds out to her sorrow.

The trouble with literature of this kind is that it, too, is
unrealistic. Men and women who throw themselves into
each other's arms the first time they meet are quite likely
to do the same thing with the next attractive member of
the opposite sex they come across, and each sex knows this
about the other. The "love" impulse quickly is colored by
suspicion and jealousy, and usually departs about as rapidly
as it comes.

Real love is built upon a community of tastes and feelings, a respect each person has learned for the other as a
result of the exhibition of character traits, and a personality
that remains pleasing under testing. Men who respect
women do not take the liberty of embracing them passionately on a first encounter—they know that a woman who
respects herself would not permit it. A woman of brains
and discrimination demands that a man shall prove himself
worthy before she accepts his embraces. The man who
earns her favors has reason to know that she does not accord them to every male who comes along, and feels that
he can trust her with other men, something very fundamental to a man's happiness with a woman.

These are some of the facts in the natures of men and
women which the glamorized sex fiction overlooks. When
older men and women read it, most of them know life isn't

like that, and are unaffected. If you will analyze these situations in the light of common sense, I believe you will be less likely to be affected by them.

The same thing may be said about a kind of promotion which plays up sex factors—of perfumes, for instance, supposed to arouse male passions, of sexy lingerie and the like. These may have a stimulating effect upon the male, and that is exactly what they are designed to have. As you grow older, you learn to assess all these things at their true value. I should just like to say again that life is not like this, in reality. Fine women, of delicate sensibilities, may make themselves as attractive as they can, but they do not go in for deliberate appeals to the lower nature of the male and they resent an assumption that they will yield favors to every man who comes along. When you have these facts firmly in mind, I don't believe you will be misled by superficial and unrealistic representations.

A second thing you are likely to encounter is a boasting of sex exploits on the part of companions, with the implication that those who have no such exploits to boast of are either lacking in manliness or missing out on something very delectable. You should not let yourself be swerved from your own course by boasting and implications of this kind. The fact is, as I believe you are aware by this time, that the youthful Don Juans are running a grave risk of imperiling their own futures, and are the ones who are likely to miss the real purpose of sex—a fine love, which will ennoble one's whole life.

One very interesting point in recent sex studies has escaped the attention it deserved. It is to the effect that standards in morals go pretty much according to intellectual levels, the highest standards of all being found among the most intelligent and the best educated. (This, of course, is speaking in general terms. There would be individual differences, depending upon childhood backgrounds, which we will look at in the next chapter.) In the main, though, according to these studies, college men have the ideal of continence until marriage, and the remarkable thing is that this ideal will come naturally to a young teen-age boy who is college material although he may not have definite college plans at the time.

Around the age of fourteen, the boy who is slated for higher education later on, although his family circumstances are such that he does not now dream he will attain it, will refrain from sex acts which are indulged in by his friends, and which they consider the thing to do. Of this group, this boy is the one who is destined to make something of his life.

Certainly it is true that it takes both brains and character to plot out a course in the early teen years that is most likely to lead to success and happiness, and then to follow it through. Whereas anyone can become a tramp—no genius is required for that! When it is your instinct to keep sex in check until the time has come to employ it properly, you are lucky indeed. You need not be perturbed by those who, either because of less fortunate upbringings or lack of intelligence, elect another course. I have seen young fellows emerge with clean minds and clean bodies from the most sordid surroundings. Perhaps they had a divine spark, which they were wise enough to heed. I can assure you they never had any cause to regret that they had done so.

A third thing you may find yourself called upon to deal with is the girl who "leads men on." She may deliberately invite the kind of advances which an idealistic young fellow has been taught—and that I myself have been pointing out—normal girls do not want. She may do this only to amuse herself, and appear very indignant when a boy walks into the trap and responds as she has seemed to want him to do. Or she may actually have no limits and offer sex relations—even urge her escort to have them with her.

A girl of this kind, whether she is a "teaser" or in fact a "round-heel"—one of the many phrases used to describe a girl who can be persuaded easily to have intercourse—is one of the toughest problems that a decent young fellow may be called upon to deal with. In some respects, I feel that she is a worse threat to continence than the out-and-out prostitute. If she is attractive, her wiles may be hard to resist. Since she is supposedly a nice girl, it is difficult to decline her favors without seeming ungentlemanly.

The "teaser," as I have mentioned before, more times than not is getting back at the male sex for hurts and indignities she has suffered herself. This often happens when girls have given their love freely and whole-heartedly, and then have found that their finest, most sincere emotions were being exploited. They determine that they will not get their own emotions stirred up again, and take delight in stirring up male emotions. This is one unhappy effect upon women of a deception that some male, or males, have employed against them.

Quite often the "easy" girl on the other hand, pursues men not for physical gratification, but to carry out her feminine instinct for being loved and for being submissive to the male. If her parents have failed to show her that they loved her and wanted her, and besides that have taught her that sex is nasty, she may rebel against their teachings

out of deep-seated hostility to them, and retaliate by behavior of which she knows they disapprove. She has sexual
relations with a man, hoping to obtain a sense of belonging
to someone, and of freedom from authority and from what
she feels are unsympathetic parents. It is not that she wants
a baby, or even that she particularly wants sex. What she
wants is for someone to want her and need her. Such girls
are abnormal personalities, and need the help of a skilled
physician who may be able to help them attain a new perspective.

When a boy encounters girls of either kind, he should
recognize that their behavior is abnormal, and stick to his
own standards of conduct. He can invent some excuse for
terminating the date—he has to finish a paper, or someone
is sick and he has to get home early, and perhaps he actually
does. Sometimes a boy can help a girl who has these mistaken conceptions by telling her how her actions appear to
male eyes, and how she hurts herself by the course she is
pursuing, in a frank and "big brotherly" way. At first the
girl may resent it. But this is far better than to find yourself bound to such a girl by yielding to her solicitations because you did not want to hurt her feelings. Girls of this
type can be definitely dangerous, however sympathetic one
may be because of the origin of their warped and twisted
attitudes. Mature men avoid women who try to lure them
into unwise sex behavior. If they must be in their company,
they try to arrange to have someone else present at all times.
For a woman with a sick personality is often capable of
charging a man with the very offense he has refused to
commit—Joseph's experience with Potiphar's wife (from the
Bible) is the classic example of this. It has happened to a

great many men. With this forewarning, I hope it will not happen to you.

Fourth, teen-age boys who live in big cities—and it happens in smaller places, too—may possibly encounter the charming older man who proves to be a homosexual. In the next chapter we will discuss homosexualism, as a sex aberration, more fully. Right now I just want to speak of the danger to normal boys of men whose lives have become twisted in this way. Boys, as well as girls, may be approached in public places by strangers who use some pretext to strike up a conversation. They become very friendly, may extend various courtesies, and end by getting the boy into a place where sexual intimacy is suggested.

Men of this type may occasionally even be found in organizations which do a fine and character-building work with boys. Naturally their homosexual tendency is not suspected, or they would not be accepted by the organizations. Once in a great while, however, it is disclosed that a man has used the entree he has gained into boys' lives in this way to debauch them sexually.

I wouldn't have you get the idea that every older man who takes an interest in you and shows you kindness may be a homosexual. And above all I would deplore accusations of homosexuality against older men on this account alone. Such a charge can ruin a man completely in his work, and usually means that he must leave town, perhaps change his identity, and start over again in some faraway place. This is a dreadful thing to do to a man whose nature and actions are of the best.

But just as an added precaution remember that if a man should actually attempt to fondle you in intimate ways, or suggest sexual relations, you should get out of there just as fast as you can and report the incident to your parents, or to some other responsible adult. The life of a boy can be ruined when he is used as a sexual object by such men. His normal instincts can be twisted, and his character perverted. An attempt of this kind upon a boy is in fact a criminal offense. If a man makes an unmistakable sexual overture, he should be reported, so that he can be stopped from ruining the lives of other boys.

Finally, I would like to give you a word of warning about misleading and dangerous advice you may get on sex matters from older people who should know better. Persons who have failed to make a good heterosexual adjustment themselves, and have either undergone lifelong frustration as a result, or have become warped and twisted in one of the ways we will discuss in the next chapter, are not in a good position to give young people a true idea of sex. Yet such persons often feel called upon to give advice to youth.

A frustrated individual may go to one of two extremes. The man or woman who has never had the fulfillment of a fine love, sometimes adopts a "sour grapes" attitude—that is, that sex is nasty and horrid and something to shut out of one's life. I hope I have convinced you how wrong this attitude is. Or such frustrated advisers may feel that they have missed out on all this because they were too prudish in their youth, and may urge young people to seize on sex experience whenever and wherever they can. The latter folk may feel that they are being broad-minded and "modern" by this approach, but it is their emotions speaking, and not their judgment.

When men and women fail to attain sex fulfillment in adulthood, it is not because they didn't pet or "sow wild oats" when they were young. It is because they have not been able to develop their personalities in a way that will draw members of the opposite sex to them, and make a love relationship possible. It takes a good deal of maturity, however, to face the fact that we are simply not lovable people, in a heterosexual sense, and try to do something about that. It is easier to blame the lack to something one did, or failed to do, in youth.

If you read or hear such advice as the foregoing from people who are in authoritative positions, you might ask yourself two questions:

1. How well has this person worked out his or her own sex life, from the standpoint of happiness and satisfaction?

2. If I were to carry out the policy of free love, and should get into trouble, what would this adviser do to help me out of it?

As a general rule, persons irresponsible enough to give the second type of advice to young people, are inclined to wash their hands of all responsibility for unfortunate results. Wise, well-adjusted men and women will not paint sex in lurid, objectionable colors, but neither will they urge conduct which might get a young person into serious trouble. Turn for guidance and information to those who have adjusted successfully and happily either to marriage or to single lives, and who will stand back of any advice they give to youth.

13. Aberrations of Sex

In Chapter 4, on the way we grow up sexually, I ran the risk of boring you by going into a rather detailed description of what is called the psychosexual development —that is, the way children grow one step at a time into beings capable of loving a person of the opposite sex, as well as being able physically to reproduce their kind. That explanation was necessary, however, if we are to understand ourselves and the motives that impel us. Also, you will have children of your own some day, and guiding their psychosexual development properly is one of the most important jobs a parent has.

You may remember I mentioned in that chapter that if a child's natural sex curiosity and impulses are forcibly repressed, instead of treated sympathetically and understandingly, he may become fixed emotionally in one stage or another of his psychosexual development. This is most likely to happen if he has not received the warm, unselfish, and self-denying love from his parents that every child is entitled to have. The result is that many people who are grown up in other ways may still be acting like a three-year-old, or a six-year-old, or an eleven-year-old where those of the opposite sex are concerned. Some people even do out-and-out criminal things as a result of sex or love impulses which have been harshly repressed, or turned into wrong avenues.

There are many ways in which wrong handling of sex questions in childhood, or lack of unselfish parental love, defeat normal sex expression in adulthood. You will be hearing or reading about various sex abnormalities, and will naturally want to know what they mean. As briefly as I can I shall list the main forms, and try to give you an idea of what has produced them.

Exhibitionism We saw in Chapter 4 that the small child displays his body with no sign of bashfulness, shame or guilt unless adults have put these ideas into his mind. When his nudity is accepted without self-consciousness by adults, he soon of his own accord will adopt the adult way of concealing his private parts. As he grows older, he will attempt to call a proper and pleasing attention to his person by cleanliness, meticulous grooming, and attractive suits and neckties.

There are some men, however, who carry into adulthood an irresistible desire to display their private parts to girls and women. This is an offense punishable by law, and is called exhibitionism. Studies of men arrested for this offense show that as children, many of them were taught that display of the body, as well as sexual feelings or acts, were wrong. Thwarted in a tendency that is normal at an early age, and unable to get it out of their systems then, these men find true gratification only in exhibiting their genital area, even when they have opportunities for a normal sexual life. These men have a deep hostility toward their parents and toward society which they themselves do not recognize as such. Often, their sense of guilt is so great that it almost seems they want to be caught and punished.

Promiscuity Some men find it easier to have sexual relations with so called "bad" girls than with good girls, and go from one to another of these without ever settling upon one love object and remaining faithful to her, which is the goal and the tendency of the normal male. These men may have been impressed by their fathers or mothers with the idea that sex is bad. If the mother has attached her son to her strongly, he may divide girls into the good and the bad, and be afraid to love one who is "good," like his mother, because he learned as a child that sex feelings toward his mother were disapproved. He therefore condemns and shies away from good women who show him warmth and affection, and seeks out "bad" ones for sex relationships, though he condemns them too.

Quite obviously, this is a very unhealthy attitude for a man to have toward women. He uses and degrades the "bad" girls, who are that way, as we have seen, because they themselves have had poor training, or a lack of love from their parents, or a need to be dependent upon a man and affectionate with him. He denies himself the love of "good" girls, with whom he might have a happy and rewarding life. Thus the promiscuous man deliberately cuts himself off from the fineness and beauty of love. He is a lonely, unhappy soul, however many sexual contacts he may have with the world of female unfortunates.

A girl or woman who is promiscuous is found in many cases to have had a poor relationship with her parents. When she feels insecure, and thinks they don't really care what becomes of her, she may want unconsciously to hurt and shame them by reckless behavior. Women of this kind, like their male counterparts, may find that they respond only to men who are inferior to them intellectually and culturally, probably because they were too attached emotionally to their fathers, the first men in their lives, to be able to supplant them in their affections.

The promiscuous are inclined to have many conflicts and are usually poorly adjusted in their general social relationships. This is in addition to the danger a promiscuous woman runs of becoming pregnant by an unworthy male; the danger a promiscuous man runs of bringing illegitimate children into the world, by unworthy mothers; the danger both run of contracting venereal disease, and of incurring society's disapproval by their behavior.

Nymphomania There are some women who, contrary to the rest of their sex, have an insane desire for sexual intercourse. They have no control whatsoever over their sex impulses and will solicit a sexual embrace with any man who comes their way. I have known cases where girls of good families had to be watched every minute to keep them from making overtures to servants or to complete strangers. This is of course a mental illness. There are varying degrees of this disorder. Some women may use some selection in choosing those men with whom they will have intercourse, but their desires are definitely abnormal and uncontrolled.

Homosexuality Of all the forms of abnormal sex that we have been discussing, promiscuity and homosexuality are by far the most common. They have their origin in much the same kind of childhood situation. The difference is that the sufferer from promiscuity achieves the state of being heterosexual, in a physical sense, but is unable to mature to the point of loving and being loved by a member of the opposite sex. The homosexual not only does not achieve this, but also never manages the transfer of interest from his own sex to the other. There are women who are immature in this way too. Both the men and the women who fall into this classification are homosexual, because their sex interest is confined to members of their own sex, but the women are called "Lesbians," and the men are usually called homosexuals, or "homos," for short.

As we noted in the chapter on growing up sexually, in the period before adolescence it is natural for boys and girls to be more interested in their own sex than in the other. Quite often there is some awkwardness and fear when the time comes for putting into effect the urges toward entering into companionships on a heterosexual basis. During these periods, the pre-adolescent or the young adolescent is likely to feel more at ease with his own sex, and timid about letting his feelings for a girl develop. Boys may occasionally explore each other's bodies, finding pleasure in looking and touching, and may even indulge in sex play with each other. This does not necessarily mean that they are homosexuals or going to be homosexuals, and an occasional episode of this kind that has occurred in earlier life can be dismissed from one's mind along with other childish types of behavior. The boy who goes on to form the kind of desirable and wholesome attachments with girls that we discussed in Chapter 7 can feel that he is perfectly normal. We do not consider a person a homosexual unless, as an adult, he has repeated homosexual experiences and can only derive sexual pleasure with another man or men, although he has had opportunities for heterosexual relationships.

Some boys are turned into homosexuals because they have been taught acts of this kind by an older person, before their interests have had a chance to be directed toward the opposite sex. That is the great danger in yielding to an older homosexual, against which I warned you previously.

The majority, however, become homosexuals because home environment and parental attitudes have handicapped them, instead of helping them, in their course toward learning to love a person of the opposite sex whole-heartedly and unselfishly. I think this is worth going into pretty thoroughly, even though we may find ourselves rather deeply involved in psychological twists and turns. For understanding of this situation is the best guard against growing up to be either promiscuous or homosexual—or unloved by either sex—the most common threats to normal and satisfying lives in adulthood.

As in the case of the promiscuous person, homosexuality often results from domination, to an unwholesome extent, by one parent or the other.

For instance, if a woman who is too strongly attached to her father has a son, she is likely to bestow all her affection on him and to seek to win all his love for herself. This is not so much because she is fond of her son, as because she herself is lonely and dissatisfied. In fact, women with a concealed homosexual tendency are incapable of warm, motherly feelings. Their love is selfish. They are inclined to be overly protective, particularly of an only son, and pamper and indulge him in order to keep him dependent.

A boy may infer that such a mother cares greatly for him, because she is so attentive and seemingly so loving.

He doesn't want to hurt her by being rebellious, aggressive or masculine—traits which the homosexually inclined woman abhors. His mother calls him her "little man," and stresses continually his responsibility and duty to take care of her. In a sense, he begins to take his father's place, maybe even sleeping with his mother until he is quite a big boy. I have known boys whose mothers had them do this until they were well along in the teens, and that is a very bad thing to do to a boy. For after he has matured physically, he can hardly help having some sexual feelings toward a woman whose bed he shares, and when the woman is his mother, these cannot be expressed. The result must be conflicts and confusion about sex and his own nature.

Repressing desires toward his mother that he realizes are unnatural, he may also repress natural urges toward girls, and avoid them. Or if he does become interested in one, his mother points out how unworthy the girl is of his attentions. Unless the father steps in strongly and diverts his son's attention to manly and normal interests, the odds are very strong that the son of a selfish mother such as I have just described will never have a chance to make a good sexual adjustment. Perhaps he will go through life a bachelor, lonely and disgruntled, never having had any sweetheart except his mother. Perhaps he will marry an older woman, whom he will expect to take care of him as his mother did, for he has never learned to give to others, but only to take from them. The third alternative will be to form sexual relationships with men.

Society's prejudice against homosexuals is probably based upon the fact that sex activity with one's own kind does not produce children, something essential to the continuation of society. Homosexuality is also a sign of a sick and twisted personality, even though the variation from the normal is, for the most part, not the individual's fault.

As we now understand sex abberations, to my mind they are very much like tuberculosis. Most tuberculous people, when they were little, acquired the germs from older sufferers. In adolescence, T.B. germs may flare up into disease. Nobody feels ashamed or "different" if he learns that he has T.B. He just sets about getting cured.

It is during adolescence, when adult sex patterns are being established, that sex aberrations usually show themselves, but they are the result of childhood experiences in which the sufferer himself was an innocent victim. Treated in the teen years, in the great majority of instances they can be cured, and a normal, wholesome and satisfying love relationship can some day be achieved.

In concluding, perhaps I had better point out once more that the aberrations I have been discussing arise from a childhood conception that sex is wrong and bad. I hope I have convinced you by this time that sex rightly employed is good and wonderful. Do you have a healthy interest in the opposite sex, which you are not afraid to express when the spirit moves you? Do you control sex now, because your intelligence tells you it is the thing to do, but look forward to the day when you will be in a position to marry the girl you love, establish a home and have children? If so, there's nothing queer about you, and you've nothing to worry about. You are that very lucky person—a normal male!

14. The Well-Rounded Life

I think it quite likely that by this time, you have had an ample dose of the more somber sides of sex. They can be depressing, I realize, but knowing something about them is the best way to avoid incurring the handicaps that maladjusted or unwise behavior can impose. Now that that is off our minds, it will be a pleasure for me, too, to turn to the cheerful, optimistic side of the picture—the ways in which you can use the sex forces to help you toward the kind of adult life you would like to have.

Earlier I mentioned that I would give you some concrete ways for controlling the sex urges in the teen years, without being afraid of them, and without the kind of repressions which can be harmful. The program I am about to suggest to you now has two great advantages. It will not only help you to maintain your ideal of continence until marriage, it will also round out your character and personality in a way that will make you a happier, more effective and more successful adult.

When it comes to controlling sex urges, I am going to put physical activity at the top of the list. This will drain off excess energy and tension, and at the same time will build strong muscles and a good body.

If you are in the period when the bony framework shoots up and out at a rapid rate, it may be that you are somewhat spindly, round-shouldered and hollow-chested. This often happens when the muscles can't keep up with the skeletal growth. You probably have a prodigious appetite, which is a fine thing. You should also be working at posture, and at exercises or sports which will give you strength and a fine carriage in adulthood.

Almost any form of exercise or sport that you enjoy will help. I have known small, frail chaps to develop wonderful arms, chests and shoulders through gymnasium work. You gain co-ordination and agility this way too. But I would hope that you would also acquire some athletic interest that can be pursued as part of a group.

Team sports are excellent because they teach you to work in harness with other people. You don't have to be a big football hero to benefit from playing football. You can get all the advantages of teamwork on the third squad as well as on the first, and the same is true of baseball and basketball. The boy who feels somewhat insecure and doubtful about his physical powers is especially likely to benefit from team sports, where he is not competing as an individual with another person. He learns that others fail too, and that he can't be "best" in everything, but can still contribute his share to a group.

This is also the ideal time to get a grounding in one or several of the outdoor activities which you can engage in with one or two others, and which will be a source of pleasure to you for the rest of your life. Swimming, tennis, golf, boating, hunting, horseback riding, fishing, skating and skiing are examples of this kind of thing.

There is some enjoyable outdoor activity for any boy, and you will pick up the techniques much more easily now than if you wait until you are older. The man who does brainwork entirely and has not developed his body is not a well-rounded person. Reasonable proficiency in some type of game or sport helps you to be a man among men. It opens up pleasant social opportunities, and is a fine outlet for mental and emotional tensions throughout your adult life.

If I had my way, in addition to the foregoing I would have every teen-age boy learn one or more of the techniques of self-defense—such as boxing, wrestling, judo. Here again there is something for everyone, no matter how small or frail. Indeed, the less sure you are of your physical powers, the more advisable it is to acquire one of the arts that will enable you to take care of yourself if you are ever called upon to do so. I am a "shorty" myself, and have had to deal with some pretty tough characters in the course of my work, and have been in some pretty tight spots. Of course I don't go around hitting people, but there have been times in my life when it was good to know that I could hold my own in a rough and tumble. If you study these things scientifically, you will find that even smallness and lightness can be made to count against mere brute strength.

Even if you are lucky enough to be a gorgeous physical specimen, there are still advantages in learning how to make the best use of that splendid body of yours. I am not suggesting that you become a prize fighter or a professional wrestler. But I think you will never regret it if you devote some part of your exercising periods to picking up some of the tricks of these trades.

Probably you have already engaged in some of the sports I have mentioned—most teen-age boys do. In that case you know from experience that when you are healthily tired as the result of a good physical workout, the sex impulses are less troubling. At the same time you have been able to observe the way your body grows in strength and co-ordination, the feeling of well-being that you have, the fun and exhilaration of pitting your own forces against those of other people in a friendly contest.

However, boys who are intellectual and serious-minded, or artistically inclined, sometimes have a tendency to slight this side of life, or to stay away from it altogether. I think they feel a defect in themselves when they are men if they do this. You may be ever so inept and awkward when it comes to sports, but that is all the more reason for polishing up your performance in some one of them, and learning the mental peace and relaxation that come with exercise of your physical powers. The boy who shirks the whole of the athletic program laid open for him by his school or by outside organizations, in reality is cheating no one but himself, and is passing up one of the very best offsets for the strong sex urges of the teens.

The second important point is one I have mentioned before, but that cannot be mentioned too often. It is to work at one or a number of the vast variety of mental and cultural and mechanical interests which are open to the teen-age boy. The more you fill your mind with science or music or art or mechanical tinkering, the less place there will be in it for erotic, disturbing imaginings. At the same time these interests broaden your vocational choice, and fit you better to be a well-rounded adult.

The third great factor is companionship of the right kind. The boy who has interests along healthy, constructive lines seldom has trouble finding congenial friends who share these interests, so pursuing some form of outdoor sport and indoor activity is the best possible way to acquire the kind of friends you would like to have. These are the chaps you should spend your leisure time with, in constructive activities that you enjoy jointly, rather than with the group that hangs around the pool hall or beer parlor. The latter group at the best is wasting these precious years. It is also the group from which trouble is most likely to develop, and whose idle conversation is likely to stir up sex longings and impulses.

As I said in a previous chapter, it doesn't make any particular difference what form an interest takes. I have seen several neighborhood boys save up their money and chip in together to buy an old car. They scoured the dumps and places where secondhand parts are sold, fixed the car up themselves and somehow kept it running. That was fine training for adulthood, as well as an absorbing occupation at the time. Boys who like to build radio or wireless sets have an interest in common, boys who like to sing or to play various instruments have a natural bond, so do those who like to perform experiments in chemistry or to study the stars. Boys who have an interest of this kind and work hard at it with congenial spirits seldom get into messes, sexual or otherwise.

When it comes to girls, the intelligent teen-age boy will seek out nice ones, from good, self-respecting homes. Dates and mixed parties with girls of this type, over whom parents extend some watchful care, will fulfill the urge for feminine companionship without sexual dangers.

I think it is a wonderful thing when young people avail themselves of the social opportunities offered by many churches, Y.M.C.A.'s and Y.W.C.A.'s, and I think that organizations of this kind can hardly do a better service than to make it possible for boys and girls to have a good time together in wholesome ways. Sometimes teen-agers consider it is being sissy to go to a young people's party at a church or a Y, but I believe that is where they make a big mistake.

I have been called a lot of things in my lifetime, but a "sissy" was never one of them, and I owe much of the good that has come into my adult life to a church that took an interest in young people. My father died when I was small. My good mother was unable to keep her brood together, and was forced to place me for a time in an orphanage. I didn't like it there, and ran away. For several years I was a waif on the streets of Chicago, sleeping in packing cases or any shelter I could find, supporting myself by selling papers and shining shoes—about as tough a little fellow, I imagine, as street gamins come. One winter day I was amusing myself by throwing snowballs at people who went by, and scored a direct hit on a dignified gentleman, knocking off his hat. To my surprise, instead of chasing me to chastise me, this gentleman laughed heartily and began asking me questions about myself. It developed that he was a minister, and he ended the conversation by inviting me to come to his church. My curiosity aroused, I took him up on it. The church people were kind and interested in the ragged little stranger, and I continued to go. I decided finally that I would get an education that would help me to be like those people, instead of like the derelicts I had seen lying about the streets.

In fact, no life is well rounded in which the spiritual element is left out. The teen-ager, forming his standard of values for the years to come, should acquaint himself with what the great moral and ethical teachers have to offer. A religious background, where consideration for others is stressed rather than fear or hatred of sex, is one of the great safeguards in maintaining control of the sex forces. In a Canadian city, a study of teen-agers who had been brought before the juvenile court for sexual and other offenses disclosed that not one had been an attender of Sunday school or church. Church people do sometimes err in their behavior. But those who strive earnestly to carry out the principles of the great religious leaders are less likely to err seriously than those who have no such backing for their own groping toward the fine and good.

Any boy can take part in the activities offered by organizations of this kind, and the girls you meet there are likely to be the kind whose companionship will help you form the right kind of heterosexual relationships. You'll find attractive ones, intelligent ones—they won't all be drips by any means.

Your choice of girl companions is important, both from the standpoint of controlling sex urges and from the standpoint of helping you acquire the attitudes toward women which make for a well-rounded adult life. The "teaser" and the easy girl stir up your sex nature, and give you a dim view of womanhood besides. The nice girl is interested in you for yourself, inspires you to be worthy of her good opinion, and helps you to develop into a manly man. There are plenty of nice girls in the world. It occurs to me that young chaps who declare there are not have looked for them in the wrong places.

If you confine your dating to nice, truly womanly girls, and follow the course I have suggested previously of keeping petting out of the picture, I believe you will discover another advantage. Parking and petting on a dark roadside is not only a dangerous form of diversion, it is also a rather stupid one. So far as heterosexual relationships are concerned, it is on a par with hanging around the corner drugstore or pool hall with the gang that congregates in such places. It is a good way to get into trouble, and you learn nothing from it that is of any benefit to you.

If you cut out this type of entertainment, you will have to call upon your brains and ingenuity to find other things to do that both you and your girl friend will enjoy. This will almost inevitably mean some pursuit from which you both will profit. Aside from the occasional movie or party, you may spend some evenings listening to records, and thus increase your knowledge and appreciation of music. If she is an outdoor girl, you can take her skating, or play tennis or golf, or swim or ride horseback with her. This will be fun, and the two of you will be advancing your skills in these lines.

It is in such ways as this that boys learn to know what girls are really like. Parked in a car on a dark roadside, they find out little more than what the petting limit is of one girl or another. A man may have sexual contacts with many women, and still not understand women at all. A romantic courtship can also be deceiving, since both parties put their best foot foremost and appear at their most glamorous. But when you engage in outdoor activities with girls, and work with them at pursuits which present some mental challenge, sooner or later the true nature shows itself. You will be able to distinguish the girl who is decent and honest and fair and considerate of others from the one who gets pouty or sullen or vindictive when things don't go her way.

In the end, you will be a far better judge of women than the chap who has confined his dating to girls who will permit him unwise liberties. You will be less likely to be taken in by a pretty face or a voluptuous body or any other appeal to your senses. You will be in a far better position, therefore, to choose a mature person for your mate, and avoid the disappointment, frustration and unhappiness of marriage to a selfish, grown-up child. At the same time, engaging with girls in healthy, wholesome activities helps you to think of them as human beings, whom you value for their traits of personality and character, and that is always a help in keeping the sex urges under control.

The fourth factor for controlling sex urges is to use intelligence about your sources of information on any subject that troubles you, or in which you feel you should have greater knowledge. Bull sessions, where boys hash over their opinions, rather than merely exchanging smutty stories, are excellent ways of testing and establishing your own lines of thought. For information, however, I would urge you to go to authoritative books or to older persons—preferably your own father or mother, or some equally trustworthy man or woman. I imagine that more misleading information is given to young inquirers about sex than on any other topic, when companions or unworthy adults are consulted. Misleading information, in fact, is responsible for many of the sex tragedies of young people.

The well-rounded teen-ager will not be afraid to examine any phase of sex objectively, but he wants the information on which he founds his views and behavior to be facts, not fantasy.

Forums and panel discussions between boys and girls on aspects of dating are an excellent way of clearing up misunderstandings that now exist between the sexes. This is a far wiser course than to discuss sex when alone with a girl in a dark, secluded spot, and I would say that an occasional forum of the kind I have mentioned is a very good way of getting dating back on a basis that helps keep the sex urges under control.

Above all, before doing anything that may affect the whole course of your life, talk the situation over with your parents or with some older person and give them a chance to advise. When boys and girls mess up their lives in serious ways, parents are usually dragged into the situation sooner or later. How much better to give them a chance to point out the possible or probable consequences before the catastrophe has happened. Psychologists believe it is a sign of maturity when young people will consult with their parents, or some able adviser, before taking an important step. As you grow closer to adulthood, you will more and more make your own decisions, for which you will be prepared to take the consequences yourself. But as long as there is any prospect that your parents will have to take, or to share, the consequences of your conduct, it is only fair as well as wise to give them a chance to point out the dangers before it is too late.

During the period when it is contrary to your own best interests to carry on adult sexual activity, you can throw the drive and energy imparted by the sex forces into avenues that will give you greater initiative, greater creativeness, and will enable you to become independent through developing your own abilities and capacities.

The teen-ager is in fact in training for a crucial contest—to be adequate for the demands that will be made upon him in adult life. He needs all the strength and energy he has to acquire the skills and attitudes and knowledge that a grown man in our society must have to be successful in his line of work and in his personal life. Abstention from sex activities during these few years is a small sacrifice to make for such a goal as this.

Boys who follow a course of the kind I have suggested are not usually beset by any desires and longings that they can't handle. But if you should be, do as really mature people do who are denied sex expression for some reason. Throw yourself into an activity. Maybe a good strenuous bout with a punching bag, or a long walk or run, or hunting up a person or a group where your mind can be diverted from yourself without a temptation to lower your own ideals. Don't castigate yourself because the pleasures of the flesh are exerting a strong appeal—they do at times to every normally sexed young fellow. Throughout all the years that you remain sexually strong and active, there may be times when this will happen, for it is part of being a male. The intelligent man learns how to turn his sex drive, when he cannot employ it properly, into activities that will advance him in his profession or as a person. Thus he makes it work for him instead of to his own hurt, or that of someone else.

Using your own sex drive and energies to build up your body through sports, your mind through study and skills, and your ease and pleasurable relations with people through good male and female companionships, is the way toward true maturity. By the end of the teen years you will be well balanced emotionally, well adjusted socially, and will have at your command skills that will either make you independent economically, or will make possible the preparation you will need for a profession.

In short, you will be ready to realize sex on an adult and satisfying basis, when the right girl comes along. That is what we will talk about in the next chapter.

15. Looking Toward Sex Fulfillment

I believe you are idealistic, for most young people are, and that is the healthiest sign for the future we could have. I believe you agree with my premise that there are many good reasons why a man should control his sex urges until they can be manifested in right and socially acceptable ways.

But you may be wondering when this is ever going to happen in your case. Perhaps you are planning on a long course of education. Even if you are not, as I write this book the high cost of living is making it harder and harder for a young fellow to support a wife and a possible family. Am I asking you to wait until you are middle-aged to start to lead a normal sex life?

Indeed I am not. Nobody is happier than myself to note that today a great many young couples are solving this vexing problem in their own way. Not through illicit sex, but by marrying, even though they know they are going to have to endure hardships and make sacrifices. I am particularly glad to note a trend toward earlier marriage in the college group, which for a generation or more has been expected to control the sex urges for an abnormally long time. The veterans of World War II seem to have started it off, thanks to the G. I. Bill, in my opinion one of the most enlightened pieces of legislation in the history of government.

161

Here were men who were mature in every way except in having completed their education, and it was no fault of theirs that they had not been able to do this. Physically, mentally and emotionally they were ready to marry and to bring children into the world. To make this possible and at the same time help these young men complete their education was not only simple justice; it was also a step toward supplying our country in the future with the best type of citizens.

I understand that now many younger couples have adopted the idea. Most co-educational colleges and universities have quarters for married students. It is not unusual any more for a man and wife to get their degrees together. Our graduate schools are full of married men, many of whom have one or more children.

Some people are inclined to shake their heads over this new development, for a rather strong tradition has grown up to the effect that a man must have all his preparation for life behind him and be launched on his career before he can think of asking a girl to share his fortunes. Many of our middle-aged did that themselves. They can't understand why their sons and daughters shouldn't follow the same course.

I think it should be pointed out that this tradition is of quite recent development, and is pretty much limited to the middle class. A few generations ago, when our country was largely rural and agricultural, parents expected to help set up a new household if they could afford to do so. A girl was given a dowry, a young husband was given a section of his father's land for his own. Even today wealthy families subsidize their children's marriages and think nothing of it. They don't dream of requiring that a son shall be making a good living by his own efforts before he can think of matrimony.

Thus the tradition has come into being only among independent and self-respecting families who have no farms or businesses to give away and who dread the responsibility of undertaking to aid in financing the marriage of a son or daughter. There may have been justification for the tradition when a high school education prepared one for a reasonably good job, and an A.B. from college was extra special, practically insuring a good starting position as soon as one had graduated. Even so, it has brought about an alarmingly low birth rate among the highly educated. If this trend is continued, in time our best brains may be largely bred out. That is the worst calamity that could befall a civilization.

Right now, today, in this great country, the average number of children in a family is in inverse proportion to the amount of education the parents have had: the less the amount of education, the larger the family; the more education, the smaller the family, as a rule. Physicians are becoming alarmed because many women who wait until they are in their late twenties or early thirties to start their families—waiting for husbands to complete their preparation for life in most cases—find themselves unable to become pregnant. For Nature designed the years between twenty-one and twenty-five as the ideal ones for a woman to begin having babies. If she waits much beyond that point, it becomes harder for her to become pregnant, and childbirth is more difficult and dangerous for her. These are medical facts.

Nowadays a college education, instead of the luxury it was not so long ago, has become almost a necessity for any young man who wants to make something of his life. More-over, today a B.A. is just the beginning in a growing number of instances. To enter many lines of work, an M.A. or a Ph.D. is needed. And heaven help the chap who decides to be a doctor! If he goes in for any specialized training, he is likely to be thirty or more before he will be in a position to undertake the full support of a family.

Those who cling to the belief that a man must be well launched in the world before he thinks of marriage are probably not aware of what has been happening as a result of this way of thinking. For one thing, it has deprived our country of many fine children, and many fine people of the joys and satisfactions of parenthood. For another, it has brought about the long engagement, which imposes heavy strains on those who wish to remain continent until they are married, and has all the perils and disadvantages of illicit sex for those who succumb to their natural urges. It requires that many young men and women, for years after they have matured to the point where they are ready for setting up homes and having sexual expression, must choose between frustration, or sex expression of a kind that does violence to their ideals and principles.

Under the conditions young people now face, I believe new standards should be set up to indicate readiness for marriage, instead of basing it entirely upon one's present ability to support a family.

The first qualification I would set up, so far as a young man is concerned, is to be certain he has found the girl with whom he will want to be for the rest of his life. As I have said before, I believe you will be in a better position to be sure on this point if you have had friendships with a number of girls, so that you have a pretty good idea of what you want in a wife. After a young man gets to be about twenty-one, the period of constant change which we talked about in Chapter 5 is pretty well over with. It is a normal pattern to change girl friends, from time to time, in the high school and later teen years. Some people continue their sampling and playing the field even longer, and this is quite all right as long as they have fine relationships with members of the opposite sex and are not afraid of adult responsibilities.

But in general, the picture changes as you finish the teen period. Romances of the early twenties quite often lead to good marriages. By this time you will know pretty well what you want in all the different departments of life. You needn't figure any longer that next year you may want something entirely different, as was the case at seventeen or eighteen or nineteen or twenty. From twenty-two to twenty-five, in fact, is an excellent marriage age for normal, well-adjusted young men. (I wouldn't advise it much before that, as a rule.) If you have found the most wonderful girl in the world; if you know her well enough to feel that her appeal for you is based upon character as well as upon physical factors, then you are justified in beginning to think whether or not you can figure a way to marry and set up a home of some kind with her.

A second qualification is that, by hook or crook, the two of you will be able to manage the financial end. And here is where I think young couples today are magnificent. Very few demand that someone shall support them in the style to which they have been accustomed. Every college community has instances of young men and women who have given up comfortable quarters in a dormitory, or fraternity or sorority house, maybe given up allowances from home as well, and are roughing it happily together in trailers, Quonset huts and all manner of makeshift dwellings. They budget to the last penny. In many cases the young wives get jobs in order to make the marriage possible, and young husbands help with the housework and babies so their wives can do this. A new kind of marriage is coming about as a result, one that is truly co-operative, and one that I believe has a better chance for success than where the husband is looked upon as the wage earner only, and the household tasks and children are the wife's problem exclusively.

I find a tendency among these people to accept only as much help from parents as they need to make the grade. It seems to be a rather common pattern for a girl's parents to pay her college expenses—that is, tuition and fees—where they are able to do this—but for the couple to manage living expenses on their own. But if parents are unable to help at all, or when the young people feel it entails too much sacrifice on their part, many still figure a way to swing it by their joint efforts. This is hardly possible, of course, in the first few years of college, and college authorities generally do not approve of marriages in the freshman or sophomore year, believing that the average underclassman is too immature for this momentous step. But by the time the junior and senior years come around, usually jobs and scholarships and loan funds are available to help those who have made good hitherto to finish college.

Couples tell me that it costs about once and a half as much for two people to live together as for one to live alone. When both partners are earning something, and when strict economy is employed, an increasing number today are achieving marriage and the preparation they need for life as well.

Of course, the more mature and more skilled a couple, regardless of age, the better their chances for making a financial go of things. That's where those teen-year interests come in. Many a girl who mastered secretarial work has helped her husband get through his graduate work. I have known college couples who got employment as household helpers. Between them they were able to give enough time so that both had board and room and comfortable living quarters. By working full time during vacations, they earned enough to pay college expenses. When people are willing to work at whatever job is available, they are usually able to do whatever they want to do.

In one case, a young man who was studying to be a doctor ran into severe parental opposition when he expressed a desire to marry a very fine, brilliant girl who had completed her Masters in psychology, a splendid choice in every way. Nevertheless, although his well-to-do parents had planned to pay for the long schooling needed for the young man to become a psychiatrist, they declared that if he married before his training was finished, they wouldn't give him another penny. The young man got an internship which took care of his personal expenses, the girl got a job clerking in a near-by store. Between them, they are seeing that he becomes the psychiatrist he had dreamed of being, and they are justifiably proud because they are doing it all themselves.

When I think of the long years of training a budding doctor had to put in as a bachelor, in my young days, while maybe some girl waited patiently for him to finish and build a practice, I wish this tradition had gone by the board sooner! With so many fine girls today willing to contribute a full share to the family's future, I think you young fellows have all the best of it.

A third qualification is that you should be quite sure that both you and the girl you have chosen are mature enough to undertake the responsibilities of marriage. No matter what one's age and condition, marriage is not likely to be successful, as we have seen earlier, if one or both partners are immature in physical, mental, emotional or spiritual ways. I know people in their forties and fifties who are still so spoiled and selfish and demanding that they could not be happy with any marital partners. Here are some questions you might ask of yourself, and apply to the girl of your choice as well, to see whether you are really ready to tie yourself down to the responsibilities and obligations, as well as the joys and privileges, of the married state:

1. Are you both prepared to make the sacrifices and endure the hardships that will be entailed if you marry now on a shoestring basis? Perhaps you feel that you will do this gladly, but your fiancée shies away from it. In that case, don't press her. Where young marriages fail, it is usually because one partner or both begin to sulk and be unhappy under the privations that are called for. The maturer couples accept these in a spirit of adventure. They know they are a means to an end, and many have told me that the bond is stronger because they have seen the hard times through together. The girl who is not ready to face tough times with you as well as good times is not ready for marriage, and will not be a satisfactory wife for anyone until she grows up far enough to be willing to share the fortunes of the man she loves, no matter what they may be.

2. Can you manage so that marriage will not interfere with the preparation for life that you have mapped out for yourself? To a certain extent, of course, this depends upon the kind of girl you have picked out. If she is not sympathetic with your life plans, and demands that you abandon them and get a job as the price for marrying her, you may pay with lifelong frustration. I would always say to a young man in this predicament, "Get your preparation for life." That is tremendously important for a man, as many a nipped-in-the bud lawyer or doctor or artist or musician will tell you. If you can't bring your present girl around to your way of thinking, don't worry about it. Go right on with your life preparation. Some day there will be a girl who will sympathize with your goals, and meanwhile you will have been advancing on your own way toward them.

3. Would the arrival of a child or of children send all your life plans askew? That is something every young couple should think out in advance of marriage, for at any time after sexual relations are entered upon, pregnancy must be taken into account. In many cases it means that the young wife must drop her college work, though not in all. The girls don't seem to mind it, however. They usually report that they would rather have their baby than a college degree. When this happens, young husbands have a responsibility to see that their wives are not left behind educationally and culturally. This is a problem that arises with the new pattern, but one that can be worked out with love and good will on both sides.

I was interested to learn that on one college campus, a number of couples had decided voluntarily to have babies before their college work was finished. That is, indeed, a perfectly normal and natural outgrowth of a mature love. As I have said many times before, this is Nature's interest in our sexual make-up, and normal people who love each other want to have children, the men just as much as the women. One young couple took out an insurance policy, to cover maternity care and hospitalization, as soon as they married. They knew that the one worry their parents had about the early marriage was that a child might interfere with their plans, so they made a child part of their plans. Another couple, who had started marriage with a nice car, traded it in on a cheaper model and used the money they made by the deal to finance a baby. Desiring a second child, they sold the cheaper car, and the husband was the proud father of two fine youngsters when he got his A.B.

Was this being reckless, improvident? I think it was just the opposite. Young folk who have the brains and ability to get through college need have no fear that they won't be able to take care of families after college. Perhaps the very uncertainties of the age we live in have turned young people to a serious weighing of the really good things in life. When they decide a baby is more important than an automobile—and that is the way many young people are figuring today—it is a proof of true maturity and sound judgment. Some day these couples will have an automobile and a comfortable home, but they know that comforts and luxuries will mean little unless there are children too. So in making sure of their babies, they are simply putting first things first, as mature people do.

It may be, however, that the foregoing paragraphs seem silly to you. You aren't interested in babies, you just want the happiness and fulfillment of having the girl you love by your side. You don't want your life upset by squawling brats. In that case I must say regretfully that you are not ready for marriage. Before you enter upon sex relations, even in marriage, you must be prepared to accept and welcome any children that may result. If you look upon offspring as a catastrophe to your plans and to your personal life, best go on being a bachelor until you have met the girl who changes your views about that.

4. Are you prepared to talk the matter over with your parents or with some older person before you make the plunge? As I said in the preceding chapter, willingness to confer with them about important things is in itself a sign of maturity. Your parents have a very real interest in your welfare. They could be wrong in their estimate of a situation and in their impression of your state of maturity, but you owe it to them to talk over your plans with them and listen to their advice and ideas. Quite often their contributions are helpful and valuable. If, after serious thought, you decide to go counter to their advice, you must be prepared to stand on your own feet and take the consequences yourself. But you should have a good idea of what the consequences may be before you do this. Any other attitude can hardly be considered mature.

If you aren't in college, or don't contemplate it, I would consider the foregoing qualifications too. I believe you should be at least twenty-one, and should have some kind of job. From there on out, what is said about the college group applies equally to the non-college group.

Aside from these suggestions, no one can lay down hard and fast rules as to whether and when a couple in love should marry. Every case must be considered separately and on its own merits. Marriage is the most important single step you will take in your whole life. You should not rush into it recklessly, the minute you feel you are in love and have found the right girl. I am thinking of a chap who is a case in point, the only son of a widowed mother. Brilliant, and advanced educationally for his age, this fellow was shy with girls during his teen years and is having his first love affair at the age of twenty. As is not unlikely to happen in such cases, he has gone overboard completely, and insists on getting married at once. He hasn't the faintest idea of financing the marriage himself, and his mother, who has sacrificed everything to put him through college, is justifiably frantic. Even though this chap is a junior in college, he does not meet any of the qualifications I have set down. He has not had enough acquaintance with girls to be sure his choice is the one he will want through the years. He has devoted no thought, nor has the girl in the case, to ways and means of setting up a marriage establishment. He pays no heed to his mother's anxieties, which in this case are well founded. He is still, in fact, a spoiled, selfish, heedless child, whose marriage would have little chance of success if entered into on this basis.

On the other hand, I would not have you be afraid of marriage if you can meet the qualifications I have laid down and if, after you are twenty-one, you want to marry. To me, the great thing in the trend toward earlier marriage is that the young man looking forward to a long preparation for life need no longer feel that he must choose between sexual frustration or illicit sex for many years to come. If you have found the right girl, who is willing to undergo some hardships with you, it is proper to explore all avenues which will enable you to marry her and to have a normal sex life with her on an honest, above-board basis, while completing your life preparation, or making your way up in business.

In all but a handful of cases, parents are willing to help when they feel that the proposed marital partner is a good one, and when a young couple show a willingness to do everything they can to work out the situation. One famous co-educational college, which believes that the trend toward earlier marriage is a wholesome and desirable one, even teaches in its psychology courses techniques for inclining parents to take a favorable view toward earlier marriage, subsidized to some degree. Don't spring it on them suddenly, students are advised. Start talking about the new trend, and the number of subsidized college marriages, so they will have a chance to get used to it. Then when you have found the girl you think is the right one, talk your plans over with them and give them every chance to make suggestions.

If parents were going to finance the education of a son or daughter anyway, most are glad to continue their support when the matter is put up to them in the right way, and when they have fallen in love themselves with the prospective spouse, as has happened in innumerable cases.

Only rarely do parents take the attitude exhibited in the case of my young doctor friend. And when they do, couples who are mature enough for marriage usually manage without them. When a baby comes, that can generally be counted upon to break down the sternest parental resistance. I don't think anyone could see the wonderful babies being produced on our college campuses today without feeling that the fine, intelligent young parents who have not been afraid to live normally and to produce life, are making the greatest contribution to our country that is being made by anyone.

Again this does not mean that you have to marry before you are through college or settled in a job. Many young men and women don't feel that they are ready for this step until later in the twenties and you should feel fully ready before you tackle it. Perhaps you won't have found the right girl. Perhaps you want to roam about the world and see what it is like. That is right and proper, too, if it is your ambition. Many men do these things, and practise continence as well until they feel the right time has come to assume marital responsibilities. Men and women differ in their time of readiness for marriage just as they do in the many other phases which we have discussed. Just don't ask someone else to pay a price for your sex indulgences, while you take for yourself your period of freedom.

And now, I hope I have convinced you that sex is far more than a physiological process, a bodily appetite. In civilized man, his proper use of it, or his abuse of it, can be a determining element in his success or failure among his fellow men, in his happiness or misery.

These are far-off goals, I know, for many of you, but they cannot be overestimated. There is no greater tragedy than when a promising life is wrecked or twisted in the teen years, before a young chap has had a chance to comprehend the long-range consequences of a reckless act.

I have set a rather hard task before you, but there are good reasons for it. Every youth who grows up and marries becomes a link in a great chain of human beings. If he respects his body and his sexual forces, his descendants will have their chance to be good and useful citizens and will form good links in the chain for their own part. The spark of life is a sacred trust, to be transmitted, undimmed and unsoiled, to future generations. That is the first reason.

Second, a nation may well be judged by its attitude toward women. When women are debased, and their naturally fine instincts toward motherhood and generous, self-sacrificing love for their mates are twisted and perverted to make them mere sexual playthings, a country has not long to last. The youth who is fair-minded and mature will treat every girl as he expects other boys and men to treat his sister, his girl friend, his wife after he is married. He will adopt for his own life the same standards he will realize as desirable for the woman he expects some day to marry.

Third, those of you who are not yet old enough for sex expression can look forward with pleasant anticipation to the time when you will be ready to have a home and family of your own, and to enjoy the full expression of love as well as of sexual desire. To attain genuine sexual attraction and harmony, together with the affection and tenderness a man wants from the woman he cares for, is a noteworthy achievement in the process of living. It is best achieved when both partners are mature, responsible human beings, who put consideration for others ahead of the satisfaction of selfish desires.

The teen-ager who holds these thoughts and ideals in his mind and heart as the motive for controlling and directing his sex urges will not go wrong in this respect.